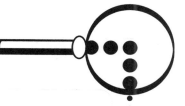

D1373687

GIANT BOOK OF
WHODUNITS

By
HY CONRAD
& STAN SMITH

Illustrations By
LUCY CORVINO

 Sterling Publishing Company, Inc.
New York

10 9 8 7 6 5 4 3 2 1

Published In 1999 by Sterling Publishing Company, Inc.
387 Park Avenue South, New York, N.Y. 10016

Material in this collection was adapted from
Almost Perfect Murders
© Hy Conrad
Five-Minute Whodunits
© Stan Smith
and
Whodunit—You Decide!
© Hy Conrad

Distributed in Canada by Sterling Publishing
c/o Canadian Manda Group
One Atlantic Avenue, Suite 105
Toronto, Ontario, Canada M6K 3E7

Distributed in Great Britain and Europe by Cassell PLC
Wellington House, 125 Strand
London WC2R 0BB, United Kingdom

Distibuted in Australia by Capricorn Link (Australia) Pty Ltd.
P.O. Box 6651, Baulkham Hills, Business Centre,
NSW 2153, Australia

Sterling ISBN 0-8069-2089-0

CONTENTS

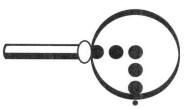

Almost Perfect Murders

Five-Minute Whodunits

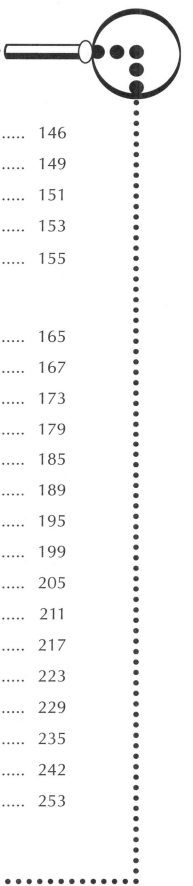

Whodunit—You Decide!

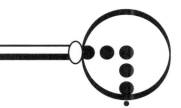

ALMOST PERFECT MURDERS

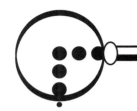

INTRODUCTION TO MURDER

It is said that authors write for themselves, creating the very works they would most like to read. In my case that's true. I have always been a fan of the whodunit. As a child, I was devoted to watching Perry Mason and reading Agatha Christie. World-famous authors, though many miles and decades away, were pitting themselves against me. We had a deal going. They would agree to play fair with the clues, and I would pledge not to sneak a peek at the end or to read the last chapter before making a good-faith effort to solve the crime.

It was years later that I developed a taste for character, mood, and ideas in my recreational reading. But our first loves are our deepest, and my heart will always hold a special place for the elegantly enigmatic plot twist.

In *Almost Perfect Murders*, I have devised thirteen diabolical murders, placing them in settings from Australia to Mexico to Transylvania. I've carefully laid out the clues, giving readers as much or as little help as they want in putting the pieces together.

At the end of each mystery are three questions to answer if you want to beat me at my own game. After these questions I give the minimum number of clues needed by the most skilled detectives. Each case has five clues, which you can examine in the order you decide. Don't be upset if you need to examine all five. For many of these cases, I would need them all myself.

Following these stories and clues is "Analysis of Evidence." In this section, I review the evidence for each case, point out the most intriguing clues, and try to emphasize the best mental direction for you to take. The cases appear in alphabetical order.

The solutions are at the end of the section, also in alphabetical order.

Take your time. Get involved with the clues. Savor each case as if it were a mystery novel. There's usually a twist clever enough to be worth your while.

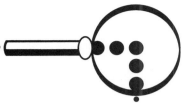

DEATH TAKES A SKI WEEKEND

Gretel Aroma was not in a good mood. The millionaire cosmetics queen and her husband had invited their four most snobbish friends to weekend at their chalet in the Swiss Alps. Shortly after the couples arrived, a blizzard hit, quickly burying the roads in half a meter of snow. That in itself was good. The chalet had plenty of provisions and the snowfall was welcomed. But then, bright and early on Saturday, one of Gretel's guests died of a heart attack. Gretel considered this a great inconvenience.

Paulina Chadwick had hopped on the stationary bicycle, warming up for a day on the slopes. An hour later, when two of the men found her, she was splayed across the handlebars. Hansel Aroma telephoned the nearest village and was told a hearse would come and claim the body. "Tonight, Herr Aroma. Or tomorrow—as soon as the road is plowed. Our condolences to you."

No one skied that day. Late that afternoon, Gretel sat in the lounge with her only living female guest, Belle Stuttgart. "I hope you don't mind her being in the bedroom next to yours," Gretel said. "We had no other place to put her."

"Of course not." Belle wrinkled her nose and checked her watch. "I can't believe poor Paulina. I'm almost her age. We're not that different. If she has a heart attack..."

Belle's husband approached from the Stuttgart's bedroom, interrupting this rare moment of reflection. Boris Stuttgart had no sooner arrived than his wife checked her watch again. Nearly six o'clock. "I think I need some fresh air," Belle said nervously and wandered out into the main hall.

Ten minutes later, Boris led Gretel and the chalet's handyman to the Stuttgart room at the back of the main floor. "There's this leaky pipe under our sink," he explained as he unlocked the door. The bedroom was cluttered with Belle's amazing array of beauty aids. Glancing be-

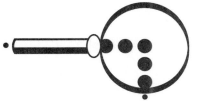

tween the bald heads of two wig stands, Gretel was the first to see the body. There in a corner she lay, face down in her sexiest robe, her flowing blond hair almost hiding the rope of pantyhose tied around her neck. It seemed that Belle Stuttgart had been murdered. Gretel knelt down and felt the cold hand. "Oh Belle!" she cried. "No! No! This ruins the whole weekend."

Boris pulled the hostess away, warning her not to touch anything. They left the room, locked the door, then telephoned the police. "We're sending two officers on skis," the efficient Swiss constable informed her.

Gretel turned from the phone to see Peter Chadwick. He had just come in and was removing a pair of snowshoes. "Road's still closed," he announced, his nerves frayed almost to the breaking point. "Having my wife just lying around... Hansel should put pressure on the authorities. Where is Hansel? Is he still on that business call?"

Gretel did her best to calm him, while Boris, the most recent widower, went off for a walk in the woods. When the police skied up half an hour later, they found Gretel waiting. "Thank heaven you're here. We didn't tell a soul about this unpleasantness," she whispered as she unlocked the bedroom door.

Wearing gloves, the constable in charge turned the victim's head. "Yes, that's Belle," the hostess said. "Hmm, strangulation does cruel things to one's complexion."

They began with an inspection. "The terrace is unlocked," the second officer said, then looked through the glass door. "There are lots of footprints outside. And..." He bent over and picked up a note that lay half-hidden under the corpse's left hip.

"My dearest Belle." The note had been typed. "Meet me at the usual spot. I'll be there between 6:00 and 6:30. Be discreet, my darling. The last thing we want is for our mates to find out."

"Very interesting," the straight-laced officer said. And he blushed.

Whodunit? (1) Who killed Belle Stuttgart? (2) How was it done? (3) What was the motive?

Evidence *This case can be solved in two clues.*

Autopsy Reports

On the Monday after the deaths, the medical examiner from the village of Hautenberg performed autopsies on both corpses and came to these conclusions: Paulina Chadwick was killed by a massive coronary, possibly stemming from a previously undiagnosed heart murmur. Belle Stuttgart died of asphyxiation, the result of strangulation with a length of nylon pantyhose. She had been attacked from behind.

Police Report

"The victim had been attacked from the rear and was able to put up only a minimal struggle. The body was warm to the touch, indicating that death had occurred less than an hour prior to our arrival. The deceased was dressed in undergarments and a black silk robe. The garments and coat she had been wearing when last seen were hanging in the closet. As was her habit, Frau Stuttgart was wearing a blond wig. Two wig stands were found on the bureau, one empty and one holding a slightly shorter version of the same hairstyle."

Gretel's Testimony

"Belle had thin, rather unattractive hair and always wore extravagant blond wigs, though she didn't think we knew. She owned two versions of the same hairstyle, one "just-cut" and one grown out a bit. When I last saw her in the lounge, Belle was wearing the shorter wig. When Boris and I found her body, I could have sworn she had on the longer one, but I could be wrong."

Alibis

Between 6 P.M., the time Frau Stuttgart was last seen alive, and 6:10, the time Herr Stuttgart and Frau Aroma discovered the body, Peter Chadwick claimed to be snowshoeing from the chalet to the public road and back. A local farmer attested to seeing a man fitting his description in that area at 6:05.

During the same ten minutes, Hansel Aroma claimed to be in his office on the phone. "It was a prearranged conference call with our board of directors. It began a few minutes before six and lasted until Gretel came and found me a few minutes before seven."

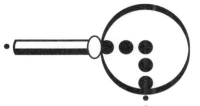

A servant in the lounge testified that Herr Stuttgart and Frau Aroma had been there together until the handyman arrived and the three set off for the bedroom.

Search of the Grounds

A constable examined the relatively fresh snow. "Snowshoe tracks go from the chalet to the road and back, just as Herr Chadwick claimed." A set of tracks matching the boots of the deceased lead from the chalet out to the woods and the unoccupied caretaker's cottage. Another larger set of tracks also go from the chalet to the cottage. Both the larger and smaller set of tracks return to the chalet, side by side, entering through the Stuttgart's terrace door. The terrace, which is shared by this guest room and the one next door, is a mass of jumbled prints.

There is one additional set of large footprints. They go from the terrace around the side of the chalet, reentering by the front door.

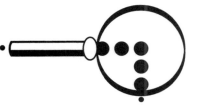

TWICE TERMINATED

"Dinsmore, you're fired!" Ellen O'Connor paused dramatically, then managed to spoil the moment with a sneeze. "Hazel told me how you've been toying with her affections. I'll have none of that in my house."

The sullen groundskeeper sneezed back, then glared from across the properly Irish library. "It was Mr. O'Connor who hired me, not you."

"Well, it's my house, not Mr. O'Connor's. Besides, I already talked to him. He's on his way home now." She opened her checkbook and began writing. "Here's your severance, Dinsmore. I want you off the property tonight."

Several hours later, the O'Connors sat on the verandah enjoying a cocktail as they gazed out over the lawns. "I hope I did the right thing. Dinsmore was a good groundskeeper but I never did trust him. And now with this Hazel business..."

"You were quite justified," James O'Connor assured his wife. "You know..." He was interrupted by the tinny wail of a car horn. "Sounds like Dinsmore's clunker. I thought he'd be gone by now." When the wail refused to cease, O'Connor put down his drink and walked off in the direction of the groundskeeper's cottage.

The old car sat idling in front of the locked-up cottage. The trunk was full of luggage and the large, bulky form of Paddy Dinsmore was behind the wheel, his head pressing against the horn bar as he convulsed in the final throes of an agonizing death.

The police drove through the gates of O'Connor Manor with no sirens. They knew how to be discreet. Mrs. O'Connor's family had been prominent in this area for centuries. When a quick forensic examination revealed the possibility of poison, the captain in charge sent the body off in an unmarked car, then set about taking statements. Discreetly, of course.

Ellen O'Connor described her afternoon. "James telephoned me from Dublin airport. He gave his approval to dismiss Dinsmore and said he would be home within the hour. I asked him to pick up another bottle of liquid cold medicine. After firing Dinsmore, I looked through the window. He was walking back toward his cottage. That's the last I

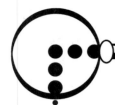

saw of him. I talked to Hazel about dinner, then went up to my room for a nap. I'm trying to shake this cold. About two hours later I woke up and called James on the intercom. He was in the pool house, swimming laps. I asked him to join me for cocktails on the verandah. We were sitting there together when the car horn started up."

James O'Connor was slightly older than his wife, small, and spry. "I'd just returned from a business trip to Paris. Got in around six Paris time, five Greenwich time. Ellen was in her room napping. I went up to my own room, changed, then went downstairs to the pool and did an hour's worth of laps, until Ellen called on the intercom. I got dressed in the pool house and joined her on the verandah."

"So, you drove straight in from the airport?" the captain asked. "You never left the house and never saw Paddy Dinsmore?" Mr. O'Connor nodded.

The maid, Hazel, had been the only other person on the estate, and her story fit in nicely with the others'. "Mrs. O'Connor and I discussed the menu. She went upstairs and I began dinner. A half-hour later Mr. O'Connor drove up. Shortly after, I heard him in the pool house; it's connected to the mansion. As far as I know, neither of them went out."

The captain glanced around the kitchen and saw that it overlooked the sprawling lawns. "Did you see anyone at all while you were making dinner?"

"Well," Hazel hemmed. "I took a break and brought Mr. O'Connor a fresh towel. When I came back, I happened to look out. I thought I saw Paddy, Mr. Dinsmore, out on the lawn. I only saw him from the back, but it had to be him."

The captain went out for a walk and a think. "The man's not in the habit of eating in the mansion," he muttered softly. "He's just been fired and is about to go away forever. Yet someone goes to all the trouble to poison him. Why? And how?"

Whodunit? 1) Who poisoned Paddy Dinsmore? (2) How was it done? (3) What was the motive?

Evidence *This case can be solved in two clues.*

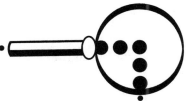

Autopsy Report

A substantial amount of N-oxystrychnine acid was discovered in the stomach and in muscle fibers. Ingestion most likely occurred one-half to one hour before death. Strychnine is among the more painful poisons, causing acute spasms and muscle contractions shortly after ingestion until the moment of death.

Inflammation of nasal cavity, plus higher than normal amounts of mucous in chest and esophageal areas, indicate that the deceased was also suffering from a cold.

James O'Connor's Statement

In a second statement, taken the following day, O'Connor confirms part of his wife's testimony. "Yes. Ellen did ask me to pick up some cold medicine. Unfortunately, I forgot. I had a lot of things on my mind."

A check of Mrs. O'Connor's bathroom cabinet shows a bottle of liquid cold medication, one-fourth full.

Search of the Cottage

The one-bedroom cottage is nearly completely stripped, including bedsheets and towels belonging to O'Connor Manor. All that's left are the bed, a few lamps, furnishings, and a telephone. In a bathroom wastebasket are found a disposable razor, twenty-two used tissues, and the packaging and the directions page for a liquid cold medicine. No bottle of medicine is found, nor is any safety seal.

Search of the Car

In trunk: Three suitcases filled with Paddy Dinsmore's possessions, including towels and bedsheets. The locks on two of the suitcases have been broken, probably with the small crowbar also found in the trunk.

In glove compartment: A small man's diamond ring and the deceased's wallet. In the wallet are 296 Irish punts and a severance check signed by Mrs. O'Connor.

Paddy Dinsmore's Personal Effects

On the victim's right ring finger is a gold-plated ring with a chipped onyx stone. On his left wrist is an expensive watch. Across the leather band, two holes above the clasp, is a deep horizontal crease. The watch appears to be in good working order; however, the time is wrong. It reports the time as 65 minutes later than it actually is.

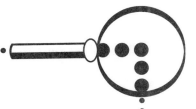

ATTACK OF THE WEREWOLF

Tim Johnson couldn't believe he was actually here, in his ancestral village in the Carpathian Mountains of Transylvania. It was like something from an old horror movie, this rustic tavern, not to mention the four sturdy villagers gathered around him. "You all knew my grandpa?" the wide-eyed American asked. "What was he like?"

Tim's cousin, Eric Havardi, was the local blacksmith. "Your mother's father was longtime party leader," he said in a heavy Romanian accent. "Good man."

Tim smiled. "Grandpa and I started corresponding back when I was a kid. I never found out; how did he die?"

The old, beamed tavern was suddenly silent. The woman, Marie Pularis, finally spoke. "Werewolf," she whispered. "Six years ago in the forest. Night of the full moon. His throat is slashed open."

Dr. Ionescu saw the shock in Tim's eyes. "It was a jagged knife, not a wolf," he said, glaring at Marie. "We found Werner alive but could not stop the bleeding."

"The werewolf strikes a wound that doesn't heal," said the last member of the group. Gregor Pularis was Marie's brother and the village mayor. "Your grandfather killed a werewolf once. Now all of his line are cursed."

"Wow! I guess I'd better watch my step." Tim laughed nervously and changed the subject. Reaching into his backpack, he brought out a leather-bound book. "Grandpa sent me this. He had a premonition of doom. He said there were things in life he regretted and he wanted me to know. Trouble is, it's in Romanian. It's his diary. I was hoping one of you..."

"Diary?" Marie instantly held out her hand. "I am so happy to do translation."

Eric Havardi stopped her. "Your English is no good, Marie. Maybe in morning we go to priest. He has good English and plenty of time. Yes?"

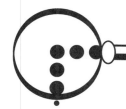

"Sounds like a good idea." Tim put the diary back in his pack. "Well, it was a long drive." He wished everyone a good night and headed out toward his grandfather's cottage.

The foursome watched him walk down the wooded lane, illuminated by the glow of a full moon. "Poor fellow." Gregor shook his head as a pack of wolves howled in the distance.

"You are superstitious fools," Dr. Ionescu growled, then marched off in the direction of his own cottage. The others stayed on for several more drinks, toasting the misguided descendant of Werner Havardi. At 11:45, the torrential rains started, sending the three villagers scurrying back to their homes.

The church clock had just struck midnight when the wolves howled again. Two boys were on the road, returning from a dance in a nearby town. They saw the cottage and the wolves circling by the open door. Scaring away the wolves with rocks, the boys rushed inside. There on the hearth was the body of Tim Johnson. The blood surrounding the gash in his throat was still liquid. The boys touched nothing, but ran off to find the mayor and doctor.

By the next morning, the skies had cleared. Gregor, the mayor, was leading an officer from the rural militia to the cottage. "The doctor and I made sure he was dead. Then we telephoned you," Gregor said as he threw open the unlocked door. But the body was gone. Not even the blood remained, only the stain of it on the floor.

The corpse was discovered later that morning in the river at the base of a small waterfall. When the townsfolk pulled the American to shore, they were shocked to find all the major veins and arteries slashed open. "The werewolf," Marie Pularis hissed. "It wanted all of his blood." And she made the sign of the cross.

Whodunit? (1) Who or what killed Tim Johnson? (2) What was the motive? (3) Why was the body moved and the veins slashed?

Evidence *This case can be solved in two clues.*

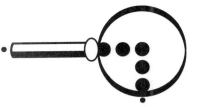

Boys' Testimony

"There were only two wolves, not a full pack. They circled by the door, excited, like they wanted to go in. We pelted them with rocks and scared them off. Matthias and I were careful. Before going in, we checked the mud outside. There were no human footprints. Just wolf prints. Between the moonlight and the glow from the fireplace, we could see. The American was on the floor by the hearth. We went close but didn't touch. Blood was glistening in the wound. We're hunters. We knew the kill had to be fresh, no more than fifteen minutes, I'd say. We left right away to find the mayor."

Search of the Cottage

Report from the first officer on the scene: "On our arrival, there was no blood on the floor. Whatever was used to wipe it up had been disposed of. There were few signs of struggle, suggesting the American was overpowered or taken by surprise. A search of his possessions revealed the usual items of personal clothing plus a guide book, local map, a wallet filled with money and credit cards, passport, airplane ticket, car key, key ring, a book in English, and a suitcase. In the bathroom was a toiletry kit containing, among other things, three disposable syringes, three vials of sterilized water, and three vials of a white powder labeled Factor VIII."

Alibis

Dr. Ionescu: "I left the tavern about 10:30, going straight to my house where I live alone. Shortly before the eleven o'clock chime, young Tristan came for me. His mother was giving birth. I was at their cottage until sometime after midnight, when the mayor came to fetch me. It was a girl, by the way."

Gregor Pularis: "When the rains started, I ran for home. My wife was already asleep and I didn't wake her. I put on a kettle for tea and had a cup. I was just changing out of my wet clothes when the boys knocked on my door. I went to get the doctor before we all headed out to Werner's old cottage."

Marie Pularis: "My cottage is far from the tavern. About halfway there, I changed my mind. I ducked into the church, hoping to wait out the rain. It wasn't letting up, so I finally had no choice but to run. My husband says I came in a few minutes after midnight."

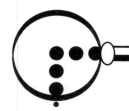

Eric Havardi: "I ran from the tavern to my own cottage. It is just down the road from where my American cousin was staying. I could see his window from my window. The light was flickering in his fireplace. Other than that, I saw nothing and heard nothing. Not until the wolves started howling."

Village Gossip

After interviewing the village women, the militia pieced together the following. "Werner Havardi was a frightened, sickly man who hated knives. They say that's why he never shaved, out of fear of razors. He was the local party leader and greatly respected. In all the confusion following the fall of Communism, a large cache of party funds vanished from local coffers. It was thought that Werner and a cohort engineered the theft, but nothing could ever be proved. Not long after the accusations, Werner was killed by a wolf."

Autopsy

The rural militia is not equipped to conduct a modern autopsy, but an examination of the body revealed: "The victim was in his early twenties and seemed unathletic by our standards. Cause of death was a cut jugular vein, the wound created by a jagged knife or by slashing claws. The other wounds were similar in shape, all delivered after death. Severed radial arteries in each wrist, severed femoral veins and arteries in each leg, severed subclavian veins and arteries in the upper arms, a slashed carotid artery, and stomach slashes that cut open the vena cava. The body had been in the water for at least six hours. It will be transported to Bucharest as soon as possible."

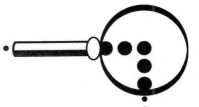

DEATH OF A DUMMY

Agent Gleason answered the doorbell and warmly ushered the three friends into his apartment. "There's no water, I'm afraid. Water-main break this whole side of Prague. I had just enough of the bottled stuff to make coffee." The four intelligence officers were officially assigned to the U.S. Embassy. Once a week they met socially for drinks, dessert, and—not poker, that was too uncerebral a pursuit—contract bridge. The evenings were rotated among their homes in the old section of Prague, as was the responsibility for dessert.

Gleason's guests accepted the lack of water with humor. Levy contributed the expected bathroom jokes, then unveiled a cake topped with red marshmallow frosting and a candied cherry. "My wife made it; so, no cracks."

"I thought it was my week," Morales said, placing a bag on the counter. "I bought some Czech pastries, Gleason's favorite. What am I saying? He'll chow down anything. Hey, congratulations, Gleason, if I haven't said it before."

The heavyset Gleason had just been promoted to Internal Security. This secretive branch had the directive to root out moles and counter-spies throughout Eastern Europe, still a hotbed of espionage despite the end of the Cold War. Morales himself had been up for the post and competition had been fierce. "So, did you get briefed yet?" Morales teased. "You know, all those telltale ways of ferreting out moles: vacci-nation scars, dental work, old tattoos."

Levy was the director of Internal Security and put an end to the shoptalk. "That's on a need-to-know basis. Let's play. Dessert and cof-fee after the first rubber."

The fourth player, Paterno, was Gleason's best friend, in or out of the embassy. Gleason and Paterno grabbed beers from the refrigerator and sat down to play against Levy (scotch on the rocks) and Morales (coffee, black). In keeping with their routine, the bridge table was set up with one deck instead of the usual two, giving them a little more time between hands.

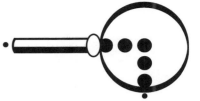

The cards fell evenly and the first rubber took over an hour. At some point in the proceedings each of the four men was dummy, the nonplaying partner. In each case, the dummy took advantage of his break, getting up to stretch his legs or refill his drink. Morales had just warmed up his coffee and picked up another beer for Gleason when Levy put down his cards with a frown. "These are sticky. Time for a new deck."

Gleason, the host, gathered up the old cards, dropped them into a wastebasket, then went and fished around in a sideboard drawer. "Here we are. I knew I had one." Gleason tossed the unopened box to Paterno, who unwrapped it and began to shuffle.

Gleason stretched his arms and wandered away from the table. A minute later, just as he was crossing back to join the others, the over-weight agent began to breathe heavily. Sweat dripped from his brow. He swayed, then collapsed to the floor. Special Agent Gleason was dead.

Despite their familiarity with death, the three agents couldn't be-lieve the obvious signs. For several minutes, they tried reviving the dead man. Finally, following a nasty hunch, Levy bent down over the corpse of his newly appointed assistant and smelled his breath. "Cyanide," he muttered.

"Cyanide?" echoed Paterno. "That's impossible. How? What the heck was he eating?"

"Are you kidding?" Morales said. "Gleason? The human vacuum? God only knows what he's been munching."

Paterno pushed Levy aside and vainly tried to resuscitate his friend. "Must be a heart attack. It can't be...I mean, if it's cyanide, then that means one of us..." He left the sentence unfinished.

"Yes," agreed Morales with startling frankness. "Either it's suicide or one of us."

Whodunit? (1) Who killed Agent Gleason? (2) How was the poison administered? (3) What clue fingers the killer?

Evidence *This case can be solved in three clues.*

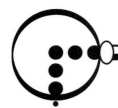

Autopsy Report

Death was caused by sodium cyanide and probably occurred within one to three minutes of ingestion. Even for someone of the deceased's size and weight, as little as four grains could have been effectively used. An undissolved granule of sodium cyanide was discovered stuck between two left molars and indicates the poison had been administered in granular form rather than dissolved in a solution.

Levy's Testimony

"I basically knew Gleason from our weekly bridge games, not much more. He'd just been promoted to my department, Internal Security, but hadn't yet started. Paterno and Gleason were best friends. They regularly took vacations together, usually to the Adriatic beaches with girlfriends. Morales and Gleason had been rivals for this new job, but that's no reason to kill anyone. Why was Gleason chosen over Morales? I suppose the main reason was dedication. Gleason seemed more dedicated to the 'firm.'"

Search of the Kitchen

The presence of seven identical Czech pastries and a single empty doily point to the possibility that the deceased ate the eighth. The field of red marshmallow icing covering the cake appears undisturbed. The dish towel seems slightly sticky. Pastries, cake icing, towel, beer bottles, and glasses were all removed for testing.

A small, crumpled glassine envelope was found in the kitchen trash. Interior is coated with minute granular residue (white). Removed for testing.

Analysis of Food and Drink

Samples taken from beer bottles, glasses, dish towel, cake icing, and pastries. Tested for hydrogen cyanide and derivatives. Minute traces of sodium cyanide discovered on dish towel. Other results all negative.

Examination of the Card Table

A half-dealt deck of playing cards is found on the table. Many fronts and backs are slightly sticky. A playing card box is near the table center. Four coasters, no ashtrays, scoring pad, and pencil. All beer bottles, empty or full, were taken in for testing as was the pencil lead.

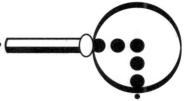

THE BEE ALL AND END ALL

The *Daily Courier* was hoping to call it "The A B C D Murder" in honor of Ace, Beatrice, Cecil, and Divine. The four alphabetical suspects were all nieces and nephews of the victim, Lord Alexander Purdy. But by the time a clever writer thought this up, one of the group had already been arrested and the headline had to be scratched. Luckily, the British tabloid was able to come up with something just as good: "DID TYCOON DIE FROM BEA'S STING?"

The details turned out to be as sensational as the headline. It all began on a sunny afternoon when the aging industrialist gathered his four relations together for an alfresco lunch at his Sussex estate. The four cousins spent the morning roaming the grounds and communing with nature. At noon, the housekeeper dished up an extravagant picnic in the gazebo and afterwards, Uncle Alexander partook of his ritual nap in the hammock beside the garden shed.

From the columned porch, Ace, Cecil, and Divine gazed out over the lawn. "What is Beatrice trying to do?" Ace wondered.

The others could see it, too. Cousin Beatrice was standing by the hammock, waving her hands skittishly, running a few feet away from her sleeping uncle, then running back. "She'd better not disturb the old man."

Suddenly Lord Purdy sat up, grabbing his elbow. A light breeze carried his cries of help to the porch and within seconds, the cousins were racing across the lawn. "Bee sting," the millionaire gasped and nearly fell out of the hammock. Uncle, as they all knew, was severely allergic to bees and had been hospitalized on two previous occasions.

"I tried to shoo them away," Beatrice moaned. "But they just got more excited."

Ace, Beatrice, and Cecil bundled their uncle into the Range Rover and rushed off for the hospital, leaving Divine to telephone the family doctor. Divine was still at the estate two hours later when Cecil telephoned. "Looks like the old man survived this one. Ace, Bea, and I have been taking turns sitting by his bedside and...Hold on a minute."

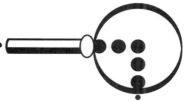

The phone went dead for not one minute but several. Then Cecil's shaky voice came back on. "Uncle Purdy's dead. Blasted bees. He should've had them fumigated like we've been telling him."

Lord Purdy's physician was suspicious from the outset, and before the cousins even left the hospital, he expressed his concern. "Bee stings usually kill within an hour, not two. I'm going to order an autopsy."

Beatrice and Cecil took taxis to their own homes that afternoon, leaving Ace to drive the Range Rover back to the estate. Over a dinner of picnic leftovers, he repeated the doctor's words to Divine. "He suspects murder," Ace concluded with a quiver in his voice.

Divine nodded. "It has to be Beatrice," she said coolly. "I read about this. You fill a syringe with poison. If the person's asleep at the time, he might not even feel the injection. Then you just pinch his arm and blame it on a bee."

Before Ace could reason with her, Divine had left the house and was striding out to the hammock. Ace joined her and within five minutes they found it, a little wad of cloth stuffed up into the faucet by the garden shed. They knew better than to open it. Together they carried the wadded cloth into the house and called the local constabulary.

Divine's off-the-cuff theory seemed surprisingly accurate. The medical examiner came back with a verdict of death by poison. As for the wadded cloth, it contained a disposable syringe. Traces of formic acid were found in its cylinder.

The prosecutor presents all these facts in his opening argument. It looks like a clear-cut case against cousin Beatrice. Or is it?

Whodunit? (1) Who killed Lord Purdy? (2) How was the murder committed? (3) When was it committed?

Evidence *This case can be solved in three clues.*

Autopsy Report
"Death was caused by formic acid, a corrosive compound used in chemical processing. Its symptoms and strength are similar to those of bee venom. The acid wasn't swallowed. That would have caused damage to the pharynx and abdomen, which I didn't find. It was administered by syringe. There was a reddened area near the left elbow and we were

able to identify two injection sites. In other words, two very tiny puncture marks."

Gardener's Testimony
"I last used the garden faucet at about 2:30 on the afternoon of Lord Purdy's death. Everyone but Miss Divine had gone off to the hospital. I connected the hose and used it to refill the reflecting pool. To the best of my recollection, the water flowed freely."

Syringe Evidence
Investigating Officer: "The murder weapon was a disposable syringe, similar to one that Dr. Purdy admitted to having in her medical bag. We asked to see Dr. Purdy's bag. It was in her car. Inside the bag we found the wrapper for a disposable syringe, the same brand as the murder weapon. Dr. Purdy had no explanation except to say that someone must have stolen the syringe earlier that day. No prints were found on the syringe."

Officer on the Scene
"Right from the start of my investigation I noticed a lot of bees swarming around the hammock. While inadvertently touching the underside of the hammock, I discovered a tacky substance. It turned out to be honey. Someone had spread honey all over the hammock bottom. That's what had attracted the bees."

Family Solicitor's Testimony
"Last month Dr. Beatrice Purdy came to London and took me to lunch. Over dessert, she asked if there was any way to talk her uncle into releasing part of her inheritance while he was still alive. She said she was concerned about death taxes. I told her that Lord Purdy disliked discussing his demise. He considered it unlucky, and bringing up the subject was more than my job was worth. To be honest, the other three cousins had approached me in the same way, each trying to get money. All I could tell them was that Lord Purdy had divided his assets evenly among them, and that they would inherit only on his death."

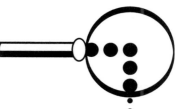

THE DAY OF THE DEAD

In the cool, pine-forested foothills southeast of Mexico City lay Hacienda del Sol. The estate was austere and proper yet somehow hospitable, much like its owner, Maria Monteneras. Maria, a national institution, was a multimedia earth mother, author of books like *Frugal Hospitality* and star of her own television series, "Entertaining with Mama Maria."

When Maria's beloved husband, Pepe, died, all Mexico grieved. It happened one night, after a small dinner party. A drunken Pepe Monteneras fell from a footbridge on the hacienda property and was dashed to death in the dry riverbed below. Rumors of suicide and murder circulated in the tabloid press, then quickly faded. A full year after Pepe's accident, Maria finally came out of her mournful seclusion.

Roberto Robles was Maria's agent and friend. He and his wife arrived Friday afternoon. They unpacked in one of the guest rooms, then strolled among the dusty olive trees. "How like Maria to mark her return to life with a weekend party," Inez Robles said in hushed admiration. Roberto grunted and frowned. "What's the matter with you?"

"Tomorrow's the Day of the Dead," Roberto said, referring to the Mexican observance of All Souls' Day. "It was exactly one year ago tomorrow that Pepe died. Why did she invite us?"

"She didn't want to be alone."

Roberto still frowned. "You, me, Hugo, Yolanda. We were all here last year, this same weekend. And now Maria invites us back, the same four who were here when Pepe died. I wonder..."

Hugo and Yolanda were sitting in the hacienda's homey kitchen also wondering. "I don't know why Maria took it all so hard," Hugo hissed a bit maliciously. "Everyone knew Pepe was philandering about. I'm surprised he died a natural death, what with jealous husbands, perhaps a mistress fed up with his promises..."

"Sh!" Yolanda warned her husband just in time. "Maria, dear. I can't believe you're entertaining a house full of guests all by yourself."

"Mama" Maria breezed into the kitchen. "As my publisher, you should know my methods, Yolanda." She was at the counter, already beginning to chop garlic. "Inez is a vegetarian. Hugo eats fish at every

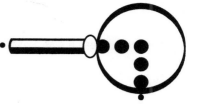

dinner; no red meat. Roberto has a milk allergy. If you plan ahead, being a good hostess isn't any more time-consuming or expensive. As for servants... Well, tomorrow is a holiday." She paused, cleaver poised in midair. "A day to remember our loved ones."

That evening, true to form, Maria served up a seemingly effortless feast. They were still laughing and talking long past midnight when Maria made the final toast. "To old friends, here and gone." She drank. "And now I must marinate tomorrow's dinner. Please enjoy yourselves." And she vanished into the kitchen.

Of the four guests, Inez rose earliest on Saturday morning to find breakfast pastries and strong coffee already brewing. A note on the stove announced, "I'm working in the cottage this morning. You all know where to find what you need. Perhaps this afternoon we'll go horse-back riding. Maria."

By noon everyone was up and wandering the grounds. By two, they were growing restless. "I told her she had to finish the new book," Yolanda whined. "But I didn't thing she'd do it on a holiday."

By three they were worried. Hugo and Roberto walked over to the work cottage. Even from a distance, through the pulled window curtain, they recognized the silhouette sitting at her writing table. "She's been in that same position for hours," Hugo said as he knocked. "Something's wrong." There was no answer.

Neither man knew what to expect when they broke down the cottage door. They certainly didn't expect to find what they did, a room empty except for a mannequin. The store dummy wore one of Maria's trademark wigs and was propped up in her chair.

The guests immediately set out to search, calling Maria's name at the top of their lungs. Yolanda was crossing the footbridge when she happened to remember Pepe's accident a year earlier. Reflexively, she glanced down into the dry riverbed below, then screamed.

Maria's lifeless, bloody body lay on the sun-bleached rocks. "Just like Pepe," Yolanda muttered to herself. "The Day of the Dead."

Whodunit? **(1) Who killed Maria Monteneras? (2) What was the motive? (3) Maria accidentally left a clue pointing to her killer. What was it?**

Evidence *This case can be solved in two clues.*

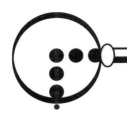

Suspects' Actions and Alibis

At 1 P.M., the time when the attack presumably took place, all four suspects claimed to be in different areas of the estate. None of their alibis can be corroborated.

At the policía's request, all four suspects remained at the hacienda. On Saturday, Yolanda barbecued the three Argentinean beefsteaks left marinating from the night before. For herself, Inez grilled the prepared vegetables left in the refrigerator. For dessert there were three custard flans and a chilled fruit compote for Roberto. Even in death, Maria was the perfect hostess.

Note Found at the Scene

"Meet me on the footbridge at l P.M. Don't let anyone see you. And bring this note. I'll explain when you arrive." *(unsigned)*

The above was found in the pocket of the dress Maria was wearing. The writing is not yet identified, but it matches the handwriting on the note Maria supposedly left in the kitchen.

Scene of the Crime

Maria Monteneras had fallen through a hole in the bridge's wooden railing. An examination of the broken edges shows that it had been sawed nearly through. A simple push would have been enough to break the railing.

The victim's clothing was torn.

Autopsy Report

"A preliminary examination places the time of death between noon and 2 P.M. on Saturday. Scratches on the arms and face attest to a struggle having taken place between the victim and her attacker."

Examination of Victim's Bedroom

In a locked bottom drawer, the police found a pile of canceled checks, all signed by Maria. The checks had all been made out to Confidential Results, a Mexico City firm of private investigators. The first was dated December 8, eleven months earlier. The checks were dated in regular intervals from December through late September. Also found was a small manila envelope labeled with the notation "please return." Inside the envelope was a hand-carved button with torn threads attached.

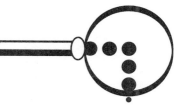

THE MARQUIS DE SADE'S LOCKED ROOM

The De Sade family had a long and noble history with one infamous exception, the Count Donatien-Alphonse-François, otherwise known as the Marquis de Sade. This 18th century author of scandalous novels had so shamed the family that they were still recovering 200 years later. So, when Professor Petit knocked on their door, claiming that their ancestor might have had a medical reason behind his sexual ravings, the de Sades were intrigued.

"There was a chemical imbalance in his brain," the bald, bespectacled professor said emphatically. "I've studied all the records from the asylums where he spent so much of his life. Now if I could just examine his private papers. They will confirm my theory."

"His private papers?" The current count frowned. "I'm afraid not. The family has done its best to keep his papers out of public hands. We once allowed a scholar into the bank vault to examine them. A month later, a newly discovered de Sade letter appeared at an auction house. Sold for quite a lot. We knew he'd stolen it. But we own thousands of these disgusting documents, very few of them cataloged. We couldn't prove it was ours."

The professor was crestfallen. And then he had an idea. "I can do my work right in the bank vault. Then every day as I leave, a guard can search me from head to foot."

Georges, the count's elder son, objected. "This is a trick. He's a thief, just like the other. The second he sees some document he can't live without, he'll stuff it up his sleeve."

Antoine, the younger son, disagreed. "Let's do it. If he can prove that the man who gave our family name to sadism was clinically ill, wouldn't that be worth a slight risk?"

The count agreed with Antoine and on the next Monday, the research began. Every morning, a guard at the Banque de Paris searched the professor, then ushered him into an inner room of the bank's highly

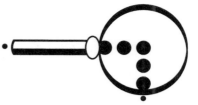

secured vault. There he locked the professor inside with his briefcase and his lunch in a paper sack. Six hours later, the professor exited the vault and was searched again—lunch sack, briefcase, everything.

On Wednesday, the professor made an astonishing discovery. On Thursday, he showed it to the family. The guard did his usual job of searching the professor, then led him and the three de Sades into the vault's inner room. "Here," the professor said proudly and pointed to a letter, yellow with age but impeccably preserved.

"From Napoleon Bonaparte," Antoine said in awe. "To the marquis." The family huddled around the small page of notepaper, "Asking the marquis's advice about Napoleon's personal relationship with Josephine. Amazing. This is worth a fortune."

The professor smiled. "The Emperor Napoleon asking the Marquis de Sade for romantic advice? I can't wait to publish this."

The count's embarrassment was mixed with pride. He thanked Professor Petit but steadfastly refused permission to reprint or sell the letter."

"Did you see the way he drooled?" Georges muttered as they left. "He knows the family will never part with it. We have to take precautions." That same day, Georges hired a private detective to check into the professor's background. He also warned the guard to be extra vigilant in his searches.

It was early the following Monday that the family received a report. "Professor Petit seems genuine," the detective informed them. "He is poor, even for a scholar. Although..." The detective cleared his throat. "Last Friday, his neighbors say he treated everyone to drinks at the neighborhood brasserie. They say he was spending quite freely."

"Friday?" Antoine said. "That's the day after he showed us the Napoleon letter."

"How did he suddenly get money?" the count asked. Before anyone could speculate, the phone rang. It was from the bank.

"The professor hasn't shown up this morning," the guard told them. "I telephoned his apartment, but there's no answer."

Antoine immediately set off for the professor's apartment, while Georges rushed over to the bank. Entering the vault with the guard close behind, Georges went straight to the desk, set up in the middle of the inner room. He bent over to inspect the masses of paper. "Oh my Lord!" Turning around, he showed his find to the guard. It was the

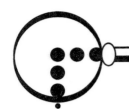

professor's calling card. On the blank side was a single handwritten work, "merci."

"Go call the police," Georges shouted. The guard obeyed, leaving Georges to search in vain for the missing letter.

As expected, the police didn't find Pierre Petit at his apartment. Hopes were not high on ever tracking down the absconding scholar. But then on Tuesday the manager of a seedy hotel in the Pigalle arrondisement unlocked Room 326 and found the professor. Strangled to death.

Whodunit? (1) Who killed Professor Petit? (2) Who stole the Napoleon letter? (3) How did the thief remove the letter from the vault?

Evidence *This case can be solved in two clues.*

Interview of the Hotel Manager
"Sunday afternoon, a man came in with a false beard and a wig and without a suitcase. We don't ask questions here. He rented a room for two nights and he paid in advance. He wanted to come and go at night; so, I gave him a front-door key. He also said he didn't want maid service, which was fine with Yvette. I didn't see him again until Tuesday. It was well after the noon checkout time. I went up to his room. At first I didn't recognize the clean-shaven, bald man. (*He shivers.*) Strangulation. That's a pretty sadistic way to kill someone."

Autopsy Report
"The cause of death was ligature strangulation, the forceful closure of blood vessels and air passages of the throat. The neck area was covered with bruises, abrasions, and contusions, indicating that the victim had struggled. Deep rope abrasions on both wrists. A contusion on the rear of the head, delivered at least twenty-four hours prior to death.

"Time of death is estimated between midnight and 6:00 A.M. on Monday morning. The stomach was completely empty, indicating that the decedent had not eaten for at least six hours prior to his death."

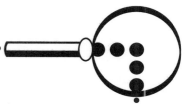

Search of the Murder Scene

A wig and false beard were recovered from a corner of the hotel room and were identified by the manager as belonging to his mystery quest.

The room and bathroom were completely devoid of personal possessions. No suitcase, clothing, or toilet articles. There was no trace of the Napoleon letter.

Interview of the Guard

"I searched Professor Petit thoroughly each time, making him strip to his drawers and then frisking his drawers. I even checked his lunch sack and notebooks before he went in. I'd be willing to swear he didn't get anything by me. I'm good at my job.

"Every morning, the bank manager unlocked the vault. I would search the professor, then let him into the inner room, locking that door behind him. I stood guard outside the vault all day. Bank employees use the vault constantly, but no one could get inside the inner room, not until I unlocked it at the end of the day and frisked him again. For this second search, there was always another guard with me. Antoine de Sade insisted on this precaution.

"All Sunday night, I was at home in Malmaison, about 15 kilometers outside Paris. We had a sick baby; so my wife and I were up and down all night, taking care of him."

Interview of the Professor's Friends

The professor had no close friends. His acquaintances testified that he was usually broke, owing money to every merchant in the *quartier.* On Friday night, he showed up at Le Char Noir, where he paid off his tab and treated everyone to a round of drinks. When asked about his new-found wealth, the professor said that an anonymous packet of money had been slipped under his door.

Neighbors assume the professor was killed in a robbery. They think someone saw him flashing his money and followed him to the seedy hotel.

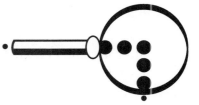

RIVER OF NO RETURN

The mountains of Portugal are known for their steep gorges and stunning views, a perfect spot for hikers like Jan deWys, president of the deWys Trust, Holland's richest charitable foundation. Jan and his assistant, Margo, were combining business with pleasure, taking care of paperwork in the morning hours, then hiking throughout the beautiful summer afternoons.

It was Thursday, their last full day at the Pinhão Spa. They had just finished lunch with Gordon Armgaard, a fellow Netherlander they met just the day before. Gordon and the young millionaire had a lot in common and got along instantly.

"I know you have to get to the Lisbon airport," Jan said as Gordon packed up his rental car. "But you certainly have time for one last hike."

Margo, sensible as always, came up with the solution. "Gordon can drive us to the river trail. All three of us can hike for an hour or so. Gordon will drive to the airport from there, and we'll walk back. It's not very far."

Gordon finally agreed. They were getting into his red Renault when a voice stopped them. "Jan! What a coincidence." It was Sophia deWys, Jan's estranged wife, who was just emerging from a taxi with her luggage. "I had no idea you were here."

Jan seemed delighted by the encounter, but Margo did not. "What a coincidence," the middle-aged assistant echoed. "We were just leaving." And before anyone could object, Margo bundled her employer into the car, and they sped off.

Sophia spent her day by the pool, waiting for their return. Late that afternoon, she saw the two hikers coming down the trail. "We're exhausted," Margo called out from a distance. "Maybe we'll see you tomorrow at breakfast."

On Friday morning, Sophia got up early—early for her. It was 10 A.M. when the Italian-born beauty came down to the lobby, just in time to see Margo at the front desk, checking out. Sophia had hoped to spend a few minutes with her estranged husband, but Jan was nowhere to be found. By the time Sophia wandered out the main door, it was too

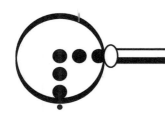

late. All she saw was the back of his head as he drove off in the rented Mercedes. Margo, in the passenger seat, turned around, saw Sophia in the doorway, and smiled triumphantly.

Early that afternoon, the Mercedes arrived at Vimioso. As the crow flew, the picturesque village was only 30 kilometers from Pinhão, but upstream and on the other side of the Douro River. The rocky, twisting roads made the trip into a 3-hour ordeal. Despite the miserable drizzle, Jan deWys decided on some exercise. At 2:30, he approached the concierge and asked for a hiking map. "My assistant doesn't want to go with me," he explained with a cheery shrug. The millionaire adjusted his sunglasses and waved good-bye to Margo, who was in the lounge having tea.

"Was that Mr. deWys?" the Englishwoman next to her inquired. Margo nodded. They had introduced themselves only a few minutes earlier and were exchanging small talk. Gloria Westin and her husband both worked for International Infant Charities. "Wait till I tell my Horace," Gloria gushed. "For years, we've been trying to get a meeting with Jan deWys. Horace is out hiking, too. Maybe they'll run into each other."

The Westins never got their meeting. That evening, when Jan deWys still hadn't returned, Margo raised the alarm. Other hikers had seen deWys hiking off by himself, but no one had seen him after 3 P.M.

It was late the next morning when a female hiker came across his belongings. Off the narrow trail, along a steep slope, she found the sunglasses and his monogrammed walking stick. Scuff marks and broken twigs led to the edge of a cliff. A hundred feet below, Jan deWys's backpack had latched itself onto a branch in the middle of the deep, swiftly flowing Douro.

For two days the police searched, going downstream farther and farther until they found him. Jan's bloated remains were lodged between a pair of boulders in the middle of the river, a kilometer from the Douro bridge, and an amazing twenty-five kilometers from the spot where he'd fallen in.

"No. Not fallen in," the local doctor told the police officials. "Hit over the head and pushed in." He showed them the contusion and explained the evidence. "Clearly a case of murder."

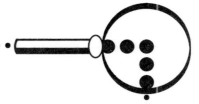

Whodunit? (1) Who killed Jan deWys? (2) What was the motive? (3) How did the killer hope to fool the police?

Evidence *This case can be solved in three clues.*

Sophia's Testimony

"My being here was no coincidence. I needed to talk to Jan about living arrangements—like my allowance. Since our separation, I've had next to nothing to live on.

"That witch Margo always kept me away—first this secret trip, then managing to avoid me. I found out their next stop was Vimioso. I got here by taxi. I didn't want to give her the chance to evade me again; so, that Friday I planted myself outside the main gate, the only gate. That was around two. I was hoping Jan would go hiking. There were several other people who came and left, but he never exited the gate. At about five, I gave up."

The deWys Trust Records

An investigation of the deWys Trust showed five separate checks made out to Infant Philanthropies, a London-based charity. The checks totaled 3.4 million in British pounds. Although the organization had a London post office box and bank account, there is no other evidence of the charity's existence. The account for Infant Philanthropies is empty and the named used to open it, Harry Weinholt, appears to be an alias.

Hunters' Testimony

The police asked residents and tourists alike to come forward and report any unusual sightings. Two peasants responded. For several days, they had been hunting grouse by the Douro bridge, the only local span across the river. Late on Thursday afternoon, they sighted a red Renault parked behind a clump of rocks, one hundred meters from the road. Early Friday afternoon, the car was still there. By Saturday, however, it was gone.

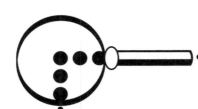

Crime Scene Report

In recreating the murder, the police concluded that it would have been nearly impossible for a body falling from the cliff to hit a portion of the Douro River deep enough to send it floating downstream. This led police to two possible theories: (1) The body was physically thrown from the cliff. (2) After the body fell from the cliff, it was moved into the center of the river. Neither theory seems completely satisfactory.

Autopsy Report

"The body was found securely lodged between two boulders in the middle of the Douro. It seemed to be mere luck that it had been stopped in this spot and not in one of the dozens of other log jams or outcroppings.

"Although the body had been damaged and deteriorated by water and other natural elements, both Sophia deWys and Margo Apsed made positive identifications. In addition, the corpse's fingerprints match those of Jan deWys, on file with the Dutch National Registrar's Office."

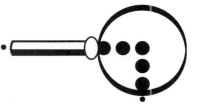

THE BAFFLING BREAK-INS

The first one occurred on a Friday. At 11:42 A.M., a silent alarm was triggered, alerting the police of Adelaide, South Australia, of a break-in at 210 Eucalyptus Lane. A squad car was dispatched. Arriving at the suburban residence, the officers found a splintered door frame, but no other signs of a burglary. The homeowner was notified and immediately came home from work.

"Nothing's missing," Doug Atkins reported. "I keep me a careful inventory of valuables. Not a gnat's hair is out of place. Lucky us, no one was home. The kids are in summer camp and my wife's visiting her family's station in the outback."

The very next morning, Saturday, at 11:35 A.M., it happened again. The silent alarm at the Atkins's house was once again triggered. The patrol officers arrived and again found the door forced. As before, nothing was missing. "If this ocker is looking for something, he's very neat," observed a patrolman. "Not a speck of dust seems to be disturbed."

On the third day, Atkins made a show of getting into his car and driving off to church. By 11 A.M., he had sneaked back and set up his own lookout post directly across the street. Atkins found an angle that gave him an unencumbered view of his own door. But no one came. His trap hadn't worked.

On Monday morning at 11:41, the intruder struck again. This time, Doug Atkins was prepared. He had hidden a camera just inside the living-room door, giving himself a video of the inner half of the entry hall and of the second-floor staircase. But even this proved futile. The sound of the break-in was duly recorded, but no intruder ever walked in front of the camera's line of sight.

"This blighter's toying with me," Atkins growled. "The next time he comes..." But there wasn't to be a next time. The door was never again forced and the alarm never again went off.

This odd little crime spree was made even more notable by the victim's occupation. Doug Atkins, as it happened, was Adelaide's well-respected police chief, and his colleagues throughout the territory were having a good, long laugh at Chief Atkins's expense.

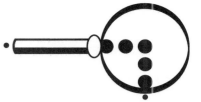

A week after the last break-in, he received a note in the mail. "Chief Atkins, For the past couple of months, you've been doing your best to get the goods on me. I guess I finally outsmarted you. Sorry I had to break into your home to do it." *Signed:* Still at large.

"Well, at least this provides some motive," Atkins mused. "Whoever broke in was somehow trying to escape arrest."

Atkins decided to review his unsolved cases and found three that fit the bill, cases that he had personally pursued over the previous two months.

Case #1: *Robbery and Murder.* The safe of the Second Baptist Church had been broken into and $100,000 of the building fund stolen. In the process, a church janitor was shot to death, having been in the wrong place at the wrong time. Chief Atkins suspected the robber/killer of having inside help. The Reverend Billy Green was the prime suspect and had been interviewed several times. Just when Green seemed ready to crack, he disappeared, never to be seen again. This happened just one day before the first Eucalyptus Lane break-in.

Case #2: *Arson and Murder.* The Bulky Woman Clothing store was near bankruptcy. Then one night, seven weeks ago, it went up in flames, killing a homeless man who had crawled inside for shelter. Traces of accelerant were discovered as was a hefty fire insurance policy. The owner, Jessica Grandee, had an alibi for the night of the fire, but she was still under suspicion. The nature of the work suggested to Chief Atkins that she had hired a professional. All attempts to track down the arsonist failed.

Case #3: *Kidnapping and Murder.* Holly Buckley, the daughter of Jason Buckley, was kidnapped after ballet class while waiting for the chauffeur. A ransom was paid and a week later Holly's body was found in the bush five miles out of town. Art Tyner, a former employee, had been seen loitering in the vicinity of the ransom's drop-off site, but there was never enough evidence to make an arrest.

"It's gotta be one of these cases," Chief Atkins theorized. "Now, if I can just noggin out why my home was bashed in, I'm sure I'd know who to go after."

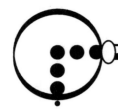

Whodunit? (1) Who sent the taunting note? (2) Why was the chief's house broken into three times? (3) What detail about the break-ins gave Chief Atkins the solution?

Evidence *This case can be solved in one clue.*

Interview of the Postman

"All of Eucalyptus Lane is on my postie route. I was there all three times, Friday, Saturday, and Monday. I usually hit the Atkins's house at about 11:15 every working day. That's just a little while before those break-ins. Now I got a fair dinkum memory and eyes. But I don't recall seeing anything funny. No cars out of place, no one stalking around. Whoever it was must have been waiting till I turned the corner onto Currie."

Review of Videotape Evidence

At 11:41 on Monday morning, Chief Atkins's videocamera recorded the sound of the front door being forced open. It even caught the shuffle of shoes on the entry hall's floor. A shadow flitted across the frame, indicating someone had entered, but the intruder never stepped more than a few feet inside. Exactly twenty-one seconds after entering, he or she left the house and closed the door.

Review of Robbery File

A housekeeper reported hearing the Reverend Billy's end of this phone conversation: "It's the third time they came to question me. They know. I can't take the pressure. I have to confess, clear my conscience. —— That's all right for you to say. He's not after you. I'm going to tell Chief Atkins, make a clean breast of everything. ——Yes, everything. I don't care. ——No, I'm not going to jail. I'll disappear. Confess, then disappear. Wait! Someone's coming. I'll call you right back." All this was overheard on Wednesday evening, one day before the Reverend's disappearance.

Review of Arson File

The Territorial Arson Squad identified the accelerant used to start the Bulky Woman fire. Chief Atkins determined that only one place in

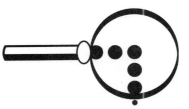

Adelaide, a cleaning supply company, carried this specific compound. On the day before the first break-in, the police department subpoenaed the company's records and narrowed the purchaser down to two possibilities, both men in their late twenties with criminal records in insurance fraud. No connection has been found between either man and Jessica Grandee. The cleaning supply company is located two blocks from the police chief's home.

Review of Kidnapping File
The only possible lead Chief Atkins has in this case is the ransom money, all of it in $100 and $50 bills. Several of the marked bills were passed in stores known to have been frequented by the suspected kidnapper, Art Tyner. One of the stores in question was the Bulky Woman, where Art shopped for clothes with his rather large girlfriend, Tina. A marked $50 bill was recovered from this location just one day prior to the Bulky Woman arson.

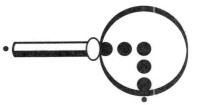

THE JUDGE'S JUDGMENT DAY

Guido Sentini entered the downstairs drawing room. His mother glanced up and smiled. "That was very nice, taking up your father's breakfast."

"Ernesto did much of the serving. He knows how Papa likes it. I'm sure he thinks I must want something." The young playboy laughed. It was true, he did want something from his father. But he knew it would take more than a few breakfasts to make the stern judge part with the 60 million lire young Guido needed to pay off his debts.

The usual Vivaldi concerto poured down the stairs from the judge's second-floor office. "He's working," Yolanda Sentini sighed. Every day was like this, taking care of the estate and the servants while her husband, almost a stranger to her, was either off in the law courts of Naples or here at home, playing the same morning music and reviewing upcoming cases in his office. It was like being a widow, only without the freedom.

Down in the garden, Ernesto and the doctor both heard the Vivaldi. Reflexively, they looked up at Judge Sentini's curtained window and saw his seated silhouette at the desk. "A man of habits is easier to protect," Ernesto mumbled. He was the judge's bodyguard although he often felt like a maid. The government had hired him right after Judge Sentini sent a Mafia don to jail and received his first barrage of death threats.

Ernesto didn't consider his job a difficult one. They were in the Gulf of Naples, on an island with only a few private homes and no town to speak of. Unlike some of Ernesto's previous clients, the jurist followed his instructions to the letter. At night, Judge Sentini and his wife locked themselves into their suite with Ernesto's room right next door. On days when the judge worked at home, he locked himself into his office, as much for privacy as for safety. The alarm was always activated.

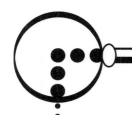

The gunshots came during a quiet stretch in the music—three bangs, one right after another, followed by a man's muffled cry of pain or alarm. Dr. Sentini, the judge's brother, glanced from the window to Ernesto, who was already running across the garden, through the hedge maze and toward the house.

It was less than 30 seconds later that Guido Sentini popped his head out of a second-story window. "The office door's locked," he shouted. Ernesto stopped running and was now fumbling for his own key. Guido saw this and shook his head. "No good. Papa left his key in the keyhole. We can't unlock it."

Ernesto's next actions seemed almost automatic. The gardener had left a pruning ladder up against a cherry tree. Ernesto grabbed it, flung it against the house and began to climb. When he reached the terrace window, the guard took out his semiautomatic and used the butt end to smash the glass. The sound of a siren screeched through the estate as he reached inside to find the latch and let himself in.

The alarm was still screaming when Ernesto unlocked the office door. Yolanda, Guido, and Dr. Sentini were waiting on the threshold. "He's dead," the terrified guard announced in disbelief.

Yolanda looked past him and saw her husband. The judge was face up on the carpet, three circles of blood emblazoned on his chest. Guido turned his mother away from the sight as Dr. Sentini rushed into the office.

"There's no one in the room," Ernesto stammered. "And no gun."

"Dead," the doctor confirmed as he knelt over his brother's body. "Guido, get your mother out of here. Ernesto, turn off that blasted alarm and call the police."

Guido and Ernesto did as they were told, returning to the office as soon as they could. The soothing strains of Vivaldi still filled the air. "Don't touch anything," Dr. Sentini said. "I have no idea how any assassin could get in, but we're locking this room until the police arrive."

They all watched as Ernesto turned the key and took up his post in front of the crime-scene door. He was still there a half-hour later when the Naples police docked at the jetty and raced up to the house, only to be faced with an impossible crime: a locked-room mystery that was to strike fear into the heart of every judge in Italy.

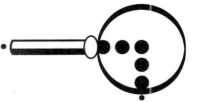

Whodunit? (1) Who killed Judge Sentini? (2) How did the killer get in and out of the locked office? (3) What was the motive?

Evidence *This case can be solved in one clue.*

Autopsy Report

"Death was caused by three gunshot wounds, each approximately one centimeter in size. Entry points are the right chest wall, the left chest wall, and the sternum. No burn or gunpowder residue is present. Three .45-caliber automatic rounds have been recovered from the body. Death was probably instantaneous.

"A routine examination of body fluids reveals a high concentration of diazepam, a muscle relaxant often sold under the name Valium. Although not administered in a lethal dose, the drug nonetheless would be capable of producing severe muscle weakness, drowsiness, perhaps even a coma. An examination of the stomach contents suggests the diazepam was ingested fifteen minutes to a half-hour before death, probably in conjunction with food."

Search of the Murder Scene

"The body was discovered face up on the carpet, approximately halfway between the desk and the stereo system. The desk chair was found turned over on the floor. The carpet's pile flow indicates the decedent may have dragged himself or been dragged partly across the room. The stereo system was found still turned on, a tape of Vivaldi concerti in the cassette player.

"The suite is comprised of the office itself and an adjacent bathroom. Except for the terrace glass broken by the bodyguard, all windows were locked from the inside, as was the single door to the hallway.

"No firearm was found in the suite."

Chemical Analysis of the Victim's Breakfast

The remains of the decedent's breakfast tray were analyzed. Dissolved traces of diazepam were found in the coffee pot and in the coffee cup.

Search of the Medicine Cabinets

A half-empty container of Valium was discovered in the medicine cabinet of the master bedroom with a pharmaceutical label identifying it as the property of Yolanda Sentini. Signora Sentini admits to being under her brother-in-law's care for nervous distress. The master bedroom suite is locked only at night.

Alibis

Ernesto and Dr. Sentini were together in the far garden. Yolanda Sentini claimed to be in the drawing room drinking coffee—no corroboration. Guido Sentini was in his second-floor bedroom, adjacent to judge Sentini's office—no corroboration. The gardener, cook, and maid were together in the basement kitchen having a late breakfast.

All suspects deny having yelled or cried out in the seconds following the gunshots.

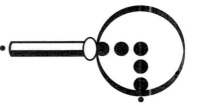

THE MASKED PHANTOM

The Botafogo Bay district of Rio de Janeiro is not the best place for a woman walking alone at night. The main streets were still fairly safe at 12:30 A.M., but Carmen Neves had decided to take a shortcut down a lonely alley. It was her last, fatal mistake.

The witnesses all testified to hearing two gunshots. "I was walking down Rua Mariana," said Gomes Cavalho, a waiter who had just come off his shift. "A garbage truck was in the street. I thought it was backfiring. A few seconds later, I passed by the alley and looked inside. A woman was on the ground, and a man was kneeling over her. At the far end of the alley stood another woman. She looked like a passerby, like me."

The other passerby, Maria Gil, was an off-duty police officer. She had been on the parallel street, heard the shot, and seconds later glanced into the other end of the alley. "The kneeling man looked up from the body. He saw us, seemed a little dazed, and then he started shouting. 'He went that way. A masked bandit with a gun. Help!' The man pointed to a side alley a few feet ahead of him."

The witnesses both came to the kneeling man's aid. Maria pulled out her service revolver and gave chase into the narrow side alley. Gomes, more afraid for the female officer's safety than his own, followed. A minute later, they emerged back in the main alley, their faces troubled and wary. Maria aimed her weapon at the stranger, now standing over Carmen Neves's body. "The side alley is empty." She turned to Gomes Cavalho. "Call the police. I think we have our killer right here."

When the Rio homicide squad arrived, they agreed with Officer Gil. The side alley had turned out to be a dead end with only two doors opening onto it. One was the boarded-up door to an abandoned building. The other was the fire exit to Movie Palace, a door locked on the outside.

The suspect, Fernando Fernas, was an out-of-work carpenter. He was taken into custody and grilled for hours. "I'm innocent," he insisted and told his story once again. "I had just turned off the street into this alley. There was this woman walking ahead of me. She was about halfway through when this man jumped out. He was about average

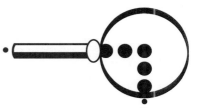

height with a beard and wearing a mask. I was still in the shadows. I stopped when I saw his gun. It looked like a robbery. But she wouldn't give him her purse. Than all of a sudden he shot her. Just like that—bang, bang. The killer started to come my way and then he saw me. That's when he turned and ran into the side alley. I know you say it's a dead end and there's no way he could have escaped. It's the truth. You have to believe me."

It was hard to believe. Fernando's story wouldn't have had any credibility at all, except for the missing gun. No gun was found—not on his person, not in the empty garbage cans, not in the scattered litter, nowhere in the entire neighborhood.

Turning their attention from Fernando to the side alley, the police returned to the scene and inspected the boarded-up door. Thick layers of dust and cobwebs gave mute testimony to the fact that no phantom had used that entrance.

Next on the list was the fire exit. Alvaro, a Movie Palace usher, listened to their questions, then shook his head. "Around 12:30? No. We're on a strict schedule. A show lets out at 12:10. Once the place is empty, we do our cleanup. Cashew boxes, drink cups. At 12:25, they start letting people in for the last show. That's when I take my post by the fire exit. This is a big auditorium and we used to have trouble with kids. The fire exit is hidden from view by a curtain. Kids used to push open the door and let their friends sneak in. That's why I'm there. I stand on the inside of that door from the time they let people in until the movie's almost over. Then it's my turn for a break."

The police showed the usher's testimony to Fernando. "There's no way your masked killer could disappear. Come clean, Fernando. What did you do with the gun?" But Fernando protested his innocence and they had to let him go. "Don't leave town," the chief of detectives warned.

It was two nights later when the phantom struck again. At 12:20 A.M., another foolish pedestrian took a shortcut. This woman was luckier that the first. She had walked only ten feet into the alley when a masked man of average height popped out from the side alley, his gun drawn. But the would-be robber had miscalculated the distance to his victim. He was far enough away so that the woman didn't feel compelled to obey. The masked man motioned with his gun. "Come here," he growled. And the woman screamed.

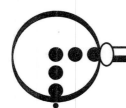

Within seconds, a passerby came to her aid. Together they watched as the gunman fled, disappearing down the same side alley. Just as before, the passerby gave chase. And just as before the phantom vanished.

"Perhaps Fernando was telling the truth," said the chief of detectives begrudgingly. "Our killer must know some way out of the dead-end alley. Let's just hope we catch him before he strikes again."

Whodunit? (1) Who killed Carmen Neves? (2) How did the killer make his two escapes? (3) What were the motives for the attacks?

Evidence *This case can be solved in two clues.*

Inspection of the Fire Door
Even though the Movie Palace's fire door had been thoroughly inspected after the first crime, the chief ordered a second inspection. A tacky, gluelike residue was found on the latch and the adjoining few inches above and below it, indicating that the mechanism on the door's inside edge had been taped open. The officer in charge swears that no such residue had been there during his first inspection.

Search of the Garbage Dump
A day after the second attack, a ten-year-old girl was scavenging through the South Zone's main garbage dump and found a loaded .45-caliber revolver. She sold it to an off-duty security guard who brought the weapon in to Rio's central police department. A ballistics test showed that this gun had fired the bullet that killed Carmen Neves.

Alibis for Second Attack, 12:20 A.M.
- Fernando Fernas claims to have been at home asleep. No witnesses.
- Gomes Cavalho had just gotten off work and decided to see a movie. He claims to have been inside the Movie Palace lobby, waiting in line to be let into the theater. Several witnesses tentatively identify him, but no one is absolutely sure.
- Maria Gil was on solo foot patrol in the general vicinity. Local shopkeepers recall seeing her but aren't positive about the time.

58

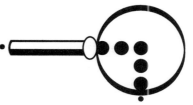

- Alvaro was in the theater auditorium, cleaning up litter and tying up garbage bags. His activities were witnessed by two other ushers.
- Raul Filho was in police custody, booked on a charge of assault and burglary of an English tourist in the Ipanema district.

None of the suspects have any known connection to the victim.

Search of Neighborhood Streets

In the aftermath of the killer's second appearance, a squadron of officers fanned out through the neighborhood, interviewing passersby and looking for leads. In the trash can of a public men's room, an officer spotted a black mask. Under the mask was a false beard, a man's wig, and a .22-caliber starter's pistol. Fernando Fernas and the witnesses from the second attack identified the mask as belonging to the phantom. All three witnesses also testified that the killer had been bearded, with hair similar in style to the wig.

Search of the Abandoned Building

Several squatters, including Raul Filho, a burglar with four prior convictions, were discovered to be living in the boarded-up building across the side alley from the Movie Palace. At the time of the murder, Raul claims to have been strolling along Ipanema Beach. His common-law wife, Isabel, says she was with him at the time.

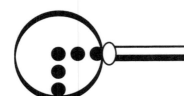

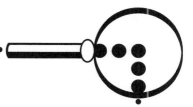

SUICIDE INCORPORATED

New York is a high-pressure town and being CEO of Yungun Best Advertising was a high-pressure job. The agency's founder, George Yungun, had died of a massive coronary at the age of fifty-three. His replacement, Keith Best, was barely on the job a week when he followed in his partner's footsteps. A suicide, or so it seemed at first.

It was on a Monday morning when Bonny Lou discovered the body. Keith Best's longtime assistant and occasional fiancée, Bonny Lou arrived at the Madison Avenue offices early that day, getting off the elevator on the executive floor and putting on coffee. As the percolator hummed, she glanced into Keith's office and immediately noticed something different. Her boss was dangling from the room's tasteful chandelier, supported only by a stylishly strong necktie. A suicide note on his desk cited the usual litany of depression and regret.

By that evening, New York's finest had labeled it murder. Keith's suicide note did not quite match his handwriting, and a severe contusion on the crown of his head showed that he'd been knocked unconscious before being strung up.

As shocking as the murder was, it took a backseat to the nastier world of office politics. The wrangling for the job of CEO had been intense before Keith Best's promotion. After his death it became doubly intense. The top two contenders for the vacant position were the creative director, Robert Godenov, and the chief financial officer, Betina Anderson. Both were in their midthirties and ruthlessly ambitious.

Two days before the board of directors was scheduled to choose, Herb Anderson, Betina's father, was at his post on the night desk in the Yungun Best lobby. At 8:06 P.M., his intercom buzzed. Someone was calling from the executive floor. Right away Herb recognized the voice. "Mr. Godenov? Hello? What's wrong? You sound..."

"Herb, call an ambulance! 911! I've been poisoned. Blast her sneaky, interfering...Hurry, man! It's an emergency!"

Less than a minute after arriving on the executive floor, the paramedics discovered Robert Godenov in the founding chairman's office, crumpled in front of George Yungun's massive desk. He had died just

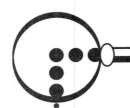

moments earlier. A preliminary autopsy confirmed that death had been caused by potassium cyanide. A hundred feet away, in Robert Godenov's office, lay a suicide note. But once again, the police weren't buying suicide.

Days later, Betina Anderson was arrested on two counts of first-degree murder. Patty Yungun, the late founder's daughter, was appointed as acting CEO.

In the prosecution's opening statement, the district attorney outlined three pieces of evidence: two forged suicide notes and a letter to Robert Godenov, luring him to a secret meeting that evening at eight.

"Betina Anderson will tell you that she was at home at the time, alone. Her father, the office security guard, will show you the sign-in log and tell you that his daughter never returned to the building. Well, who can blame a father for protecting his child? But this time, Ms. Anderson left us some clues.

"First," the district attorney held up an evidence bag, "a typed letter found in Mr. Godenov's bottom drawer in which Ms. Anderson set up their last fatal appointment. And then, even more damning..." A second evidence bag. "This so-called suicide note, written on the same paper and with the same pen as Keith Best's forged suicide note. It all fits together. Betina Anderson lured Robert Godenov back to the office, poisoned his coffee with cyanide, then made her escape, planting a suicide note on his desk.

"But Robert Godenov did not die as quickly as he was supposed to. His recorded call down to the security desk reveals a diabolical plot engineered by a 'sneaky, interfering' woman, the victim's own words. Ladies and gentlemen, that woman is Betina Anderson."

Whodunit? (1) Who killed Keith Best? (2) Who killed Robert Godenov? (3) How did Robert Godenov ingest the cyanide?

Evidence *This case can be solved in two clues.*

Holographic Expert
"The Keith Best suicide note is the better of the two forgeries and resembles Mr. Best's handwriting in most of the details. The second example, the Godenov suicide note, was definitely written by the same

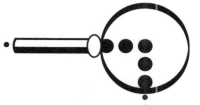

person. There are aspects of this note that mirror Mr. Godenov's hand. Other aspects clearly indicate Ms. Anderson's writing."

The Godenov suicide Note:

"To Whom It May Concern,

The police will soon discover the truth, that I murdered Keith. I wanted so desperately to become CEO. I can no longer live with the guilt and I would rather die than face the inevitable exposure and shame. I ask my friends and the Best family to forgive me." *(unsigned)*

Appointment Letter

This typewritten letter was found in a plain, sealed envelope in Robert Godenov's bottom-right drawer.

"We've both been promised things by Yungun Best and we've both been passed over and treated shabbily. Suddenly, we're in a good position and (who knows?) there may be some advantage in combining forces. Meet me tonight. Eight. In my office. I don't have to tell you to keep this secret. *(signed)* B."

Cleaning Lady's Testimony

"I was on the executive floor a few minutes before eight, taking a break. I made myself a cup of coffee and was searching for some sweetener. They were all out of saccharine, but some of them keep a few packets hidden away. Anyway, I had just found a partly used packet somewhere and was about to use it when I heard the elevator. I didn't want anyone to see me goofing off; so, I left everything on the counter, then took my mop and pail and hit the stairs to the next floor. As I walked up, I could hear Mr. Godenov's voice, kind of mumbling. I know him 'cause he sometimes works late. I don't know if he was talking to himself or someone else. I didn't hear anyone else."

Paramedic on the Scene

"We found Mr. Godenov's body in Mr. Yungun's old office. Several drawers were open and their contents scattered. It looked like Mr. Godenov had been looking for something. As I was trying to revive him, I noticed an ampoule of amyl nitrite in his hand. I found out later that the late Mr. Yungun had a heart condition and kept amyl nitrite in the office just in case he had an attack. Now, amyl nitrite is a kind of

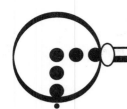

low-level antidote for cyanide. Mr. Godenov must have known he'd been poisoned. He also knew the antidote, and was trying to inhale some when he died."

Officer on the Scene
"On the coffee counter, I found two mugs of coffee, both relatively hot. One was black, unsweetened. No prints. The other was about half full. Black, unsweetened, mixed with potassium cyanide. Victim's prints on the cup. Also on the counter was a coffee stirrer. Wet. Plus an open jar of instant coffee. The other things, sugar packets and stuff; none of it looked like it had been touched. The trash can was fairly full. Leftovers from the work day.

"I checked the security log downstairs in the lobby. It showed Mr. Godenov signing in at 7:55. No other sign-ins."

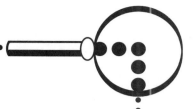

DEATH OF THE SALESMEN

Barry Naybors was busy raking up leaves when he heard the scream. It was coming from the thick patch of trees behind his house. By the time Barry threw down his rake and ran up the wooded path, the piercing shriek had stopped. Little Nellie Shell stood frozen in the middle of the path, ready to scream again. "Nellie, what's the matter?"

The 11-year-old pointed. A blood-stained shirt hung from a low branch, blocking the path. Barry looked past the shirt and saw what had made Nellie scream. It was a man staring blankly up at them from the bottom of a ravine. They were close enough to make an identification. The thick, black-frame glasses, the colorful tattoo on the left forearm, the balding head. "It's Mr. Chirac," Nellie wailed. "See the knife?" Barry saw. A kitchen knife protruded gruesomely from a gash in Joël Chirac's bare chest.

Fifteen minutes later, the Toronto police arrived at Barry Naybors' house. "I took Nellie home," the long-haul trucker explained as he led the troopers to the site. "She's been told a hundred times not to use the woods as a shortcut to school. But you know kids. The bloody shirt is..." Barry paused and looked around. "It's gone."

Not only was the shirt gone, but so was the body. A trooper lowered himself into the ravine and began to inspect the flattened branches. "Are you sure you really saw..." Then his eyes fell on the bloody steak knife.

At the local hospital, Annette Chirac was nearing the end of her shift. Annette was French Canadian, like her husband of two years. Both were known to speak passable English. "Joël works for a drug company," the petite nurse said. "He left this morning on one of his sales trips. Is anything wrong?"

The senior trooper gently explained the situation. "My poor, foolish..." Annette wrung her hands. "I told him to take those threats seriously."

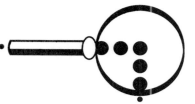

"Threats?" The trooper perked up. "What threats?"

Back at home, Annette showed them a trio of letters, all promising Joël Chirac that he would soon die. "The first came last month. Once, when he was on the road, I got a phone call. A man whispering—same sort of thing. There didn't seem to be any motive; so, Joël never took them seriously."

The police launched an intensive investigation. The only clue, a bloody fingerprint on the knife, was put through the department's AFIS computer and miraculously came up with a match. Nathaniel Sims, a sales representative for a rival drug company, had his prints on file, the result of a traffic arrest years earlier. Sims lived 170 kilometers away and had no known association with Joël Chirac.

Sims was brought in for questioning. He seemed shy and harmless and claimed to have no idea how his prints could have gotten on the knife. The police couldn't help noticing the tissue paper stuffed up one nostril. "I've been having a lot of nosebleeds lately," the timid suspect explained. "It's just nerves."

The next day, they placed Sims in a lineup, hoping Chirac's wife could identify him. As Annette Chirac studied the faces, her eyes kept returning to Sims. Suddenly she was nervous. Several times Annette seemed about to speak, but never did. And she never made an identification.

Just a few hours after the lineup, the police had their evidence. The blood on the weapon match Sim's blood type. Also, a check of phone records showed a call from the Sims house to Chirac's on the same day Annette received the phone threat.

When the police arrived with an arrest warrant, Betty Sims invited them in. "Nathaniel just left. Moose season starts tomorrow. He never misses it, except when he's on some sales trip. He camps out the night before, just to get an early start. I don't know exactly where."

An all-points-bulletin described Nathaniel Sim's car. Shortly after dawn, a Mountie spotted the tan Pontiac in a roadside turnout. He trudged up the nearest path and soon found his man at a campsite. Nathaniel Sims was still half-zipped into his sleeping bag, held in place by a steak knife that looked suspiciously like the knife used on Joël Chirac. Dead.

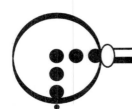

Whodunit? (1) What happened to Joël Chirac? (2) Who killed Nathaniel Sims? (3) What clue connects the killer to the crime?

Evidence *This case can be solved in one clue.*

Interview and Alibis

Barry Naybors had just returned from a long haul into the hinterlands of New Brunswick. "Been driving for two days. I pulled my rig into the dock about six this morning, then went home to bed." Naybors was asked about his friendship with Annette Chirac. "Her husband was on the road a lot. When I was home, she used to come over and talk." He scraped the caked dirt out from under his fingernails. "I guess she was pretty lonely."

The police questioned Annette Chirac at the hospital, just as she was leaving work. "After I got home from the lineup, I went right to bed. I got up at eleven and arrived here at midnight when my shift began." Annette seemed nervous. Her hands fumbled with the buttons on the right side of her oversized red parka as she buttoned it up.

Betty Sims described her evening. "Nathaniel packed up the Pontiac and left around eight. I kissed him good-bye at the curb. There was another car. It started up and drove off a few seconds after Nathaniel. I didn't see what type or color." The widow fingered the keys of her own car, a white Toyota. "I didn't mention this last night because it didn't seem important."

Information about Victims

Nathaniel Sims was born into a French-English family in Montréal and is survived by his wife of eleven years, two sons, and his mother. For the past ten years, Sims worked for Maxxon Drugs, and his sales territory encompassed a 250-kilometer radius of Toronto.

Joël Chirac was an orphan raised in Québec, Québec, by relatives now deceased. According to Annette, they met in Toronto two and a half years ago. Shortly thereafter, Joël acquired his sales job at Walling Pharmaceutical. The police are currently checking out Chirac's previous job history.

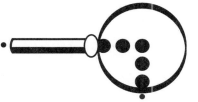

While Joël Chirac was a bold, flashy dresser, Nathaniel Sims was conservative in taste. Both were about the same age, and their territories covered approximately the same area.

Wills and Insurance
Shortly after their husbands' deaths, Annette Chirac and Betty Sims filed insurance claims. Since their husbands both died from acts of violence, both widows were entitled to double indemnity, double the normal payoff. The policies were part of the benefits package provided by the men's employers and would pay out $500,000 apiece. Both widows were the sole beneficiaries.

Campsite Investigation
The scene of Nathaniel Sim's murder is 35 kilometers from the Sims residence and 150 kilometers from the Chirac residence. An inspection of the campfire ashes revealed the charred remains of a small, heavy green jacket. No other outerwear was discovered at the site, leading to the assumption that the killer burned the deceased's coat.

The deceased was clean-shaven with an old scar on his left forearm. A preliminary examination indicated cause of death to have been a single stab wound to the heart. The deceased's sleeping bag and the surrounding few feet were saturated with blood. A toupee was found among the deceased's possessions. Mrs. Sims and various neighbors confirmed the fact that, for the past ten years at least, the deceased was in the habit of wearing a hairpiece.

Search for Joël Chirac's Car
Annette Chirac testified that her husband drove off on a business trip the morning of his murder. Mme. Chirac described his car as a late-model tan Pontiac but was unable to supply police with the license number. An inspection of the deceased's papers have failed to turn up registration or ownership papers, and to date, no trace of the car has been found.

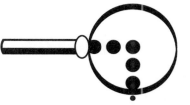

ANALYSIS OF EVIDENCE

Stories are in alphabetical order.

Attack of the Werewolf

The slashed throat, the presence of wolves, and the absence of human footprints start the local peasantry whispering about werewolves. But there are mysteries here that can't be blamed on the supernatural. For instance, why was the blood mopped up from the cottage floor? Why was the body moved to the river? What is Factor VIII? And why did someone mutilate the already dead corpse?

    The list of the American's possessions is notable not only for what it contained but for what it didn't contain. The absence of one item from the cottage points directly to a strong motive.

    Only Dr. Ionescu has an alibi for the fifteen minutes prior to the body's discovery. On the other hand, Ionescu is the only suspect without an alibi from 10:30 to 11:00.

The Baffling Break-ins

Here are the facts we have to go on. The break-ins occurred on Friday, Saturday, and Monday between 11:30 and noon, shortly after the mail delivery. Nothing was stolen or disturbed, and on the last occasion the intruder did not take more than a few steps inside. Since this was the intruder's last foray into the house, we can probably assume that the intruder accomplished his or her mission with this final, minimal entry.

    The connection between Art Tyner, the suspected kidnapper, and the Bulky Woman store, the site of the arson, appears tenuous. His girlfriend, Tina, was "big-boned" and likely to have shopped at this store. The fact that the cleaning supply company that was the source of the accelerant used for arson is only two blocks from the chief's home also appears coincidental.

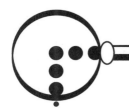

The Bee All and End All

Four points seem worthy of investigation: honey, the puncture marks, time, and the groundskeeper.

First off, the honey. Why would Beatrice risk exposure by doing something so risky as coating the hammock bottom with honey? The bee-sting story would have been almost as convincing without a lot of bees humming around.

Next comes the puzzle of the double puncture wounds. Had the first one been a mistake, a slip of the hand? It's possible. But there just might be another explanation.

The third question, time. Would Beatrice have had enough time after the supposed bee sting to wipe off the syringe and dispose of it in the garden hose?

And finally, there's the groundskeeper. If he's telling the truth, then the syringe had not been shoved up the hose until after Beatrice left to accompany her uncle to the hospital. This points to a frame-up by one of the other cousins. The lack of fingerprints on the syringe also points to this. Wiped-off prints mean the killer was expecting the weapon to be found, something Bea would not have planned on.

The Day of the Dead

On the day before the murder, Hugo made a good point. Plenty of people, men and women, could have motives for killing Maria's late husband.

The location and date of Maria's murder, replicating those of her husband's death, are too great to be labeled a coincidence. Also, the fact that the footbridge railing had been sawed through makes this murder seem well planned.

The two notes were either both written by the killer or by Maria herself. Likewise, the mannequin had either been placed at the window by the killer or by Maria. The most logical reason would be to provide an alibi or to disguise the time of death.

As for Maria, several facts seem significant. The weekend party mirroring the party from a year ago, the employment of private investigators, the torn-off button—all these point to the hostess's involvement in some secret plan.

On close examination, Maria's frugal but organized system of entertaining may provide a pivotal clue to her killer's identity.

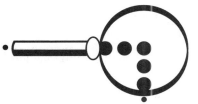

Death of a Dummy

Due to lack of an obvious motive, the best approach might be to concentrate on the physical evidence first.

The poison took effect in one to three minutes, logically placing the victim in the kitchen at the time of ingestion. A granule was found in his teeth, indicating that the poison had not been dissolved in a liquid. Since no cyanide was discovered in any foodstuffs, it's probable that the victim ate the only tainted item. This eliminates the identical minipastries, since the killer had no way of knowing which one the victim would filch. The presence of cyanide traces on the dish towel leads to the assumption that either the killer or victim wiped his hands on the towel after touching the poison.

The sticky cards present an interesting problem. How did the cards get sticky?

Death of the Salesmen

The two victims had several things in common. They were about the same age, originally from Québec and employed as pharmaceutical sales reps. Both drove similar cars and were killed with similar knives. Both were insured with double-indemnity policies, although this can be explained by the fact that they worked for companies with similar benefits packages.

The bloody fingerprints on the knife and the phone call point to some connection between Sims and Chirac. But while Sim's background seems fairly straightforward, Chirac's personal history only seems to date back two and a half years.

The green jacket remnants found in the ashes are puzzling, since only a rather foolish hunter would dress in green. Red and orange tend to be the hunter's colors of choice.

One other oddity. Why would a killer leave Joël Chirac's shirt on a branch blocking the path? Perhaps the body was meant to be found by the schoolgirl who regularly took that shortcut.

Death Takes a Ski Weekend

The footprints tell us that Belle walked out to the caretaker's cottage, perhaps for a romantic rendezvous. There she met someone who accompanied her back to the chalet, where she apparently changed both her wig and her clothes.

There are two discrepancies in the physical evidence. (1) Gretel testified that Belle's hand was cold. Half an hour later, the police found the victim still warm. (2) When the witnesses first saw them, both wig stands were empty. On the police's arrival, however, the shorter-styled wig was back on its stand. Clearly, someone had been on the murder scene between the discovery of the body and the arrival of the police.

The murder seems to have happened within a 10-minute time frame during which everyone had an ironclad alibi. This suggests that the murder may not have occurred within that limited time.

The Judge's Judgment Day

Everyone in the house had access to the diazepam. The three suspects who could have most easily placed it in the judge's coffee are Yolanda, who brewed it; Ernesto, who arranged the breakfast tray; and Guido, who poured the judge's first cup.

The huge, frightening puzzle of the murder—how an unseen killer could get in, get out, and dispose of his gun without being seen or triggering the alarm—can be broken down into a series of smaller puzzles.

The first is the man's muffled cry heard just after the gunshots. It had to come either from Guido or from the judge himself. Guido denies having made any such sound, and the autopsy indicates that the judge died almost instantly.

The next puzzle involves the dragged body. If the judge dragged himself, then his death was not instantaneous. If, on the other hand, the killer dragged him, he or she must have had a good reason for taking valuable time to do this.

The presence of diazepam in the judge's system brings up the third puzzle. Why? If the killer just wanted to kill, why didn't he or she use a more effective poison? It would have been much less risky than a shooting. Or why not just shoot the judge without the poison? Why were both methods necessary?

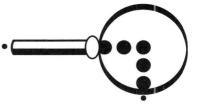

The Marquis de Sade's Locked Room

Since the Napoléon letter is still missing and there seems to be no other reason to kill Professor Petit, we can assume that possession of the letter is the motive behind the murder.

The absence of luggage and the lack of personal effects in the room seem puzzling, even when taking into account that the victim was on the lam and traveling light. The most logical explanation is that someone other than the professor rented the room.

But the crux of this case lies in how *anyone* could have removed the Napoléon letter from the inner room. Once this mystery is fathomed, we'll probably have all the answers we need.

The professor certainly seems implicated. His free-spending ways on Friday night, his flight to a hotel on Sunday, and his calling card left on the table all point to this. And yet,...if Professor Petit had been planning to steal the letter, why did he bother to tell the de Sade family about its existence? That seems counterproductive.

The bank guard cannot be completely ruled out as an accomplice, although he does have an alibi for the time of the professor's murder.

The Masked Phantom

The presence of the garbage truck on Rua Mariana at the time of the first attack suggests a simple way for the killer to dispose of the first gun. Simply toss it into a garbage bag or into the truck itself. This is supported by the discovery of the gun days later in a garbage dump.

The dust and cobwebs on the boarded-up door rule out the abandoned building as a means of escape, and that leaves the movie theater as the only plausible route. The tape residue on the latch reveals that the fire door had been used for the second escape. The phantom probably sneaked in while the ushers were cleaning and hid behind the curtain until the auditorium started filling up. But to do this, the killer had to be aware of the theater's schedule.

For the first escape to work, however, (a) the police had to be wrong about the lack of tape residue and (b) Alvaro the usher had to be involved. Either that, or Fernando lied about the killer running into the side alley. The possibility also exists that Fernando was simply mistaken. Perhaps he'd been so preoccupied with the murdered woman that he didn't really see the masked killer leave.

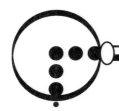

The most puzzling puzzle, however, may be the disguise. If the police had found the gun on the killer after the first attack, that would have been an incriminating piece of evidence. That's why the killer got rid of it. But the disguise would have been just as incriminating. So, why didn't the killer dispose of the disguise at the same time?

River of No Return

There appear to be only two possible motives: one, inheritance, since his wife, Sophia profited from Jan's death, or two, fraud. Infant Philanthropies could be a concoction of Margo's or of the Westins', who run an English charity with a similar name.

There is one glaring discrepancy in testimony. Sophia testified that Jan did not leave the hotel gates between 2 P.M. and 5 P.M. But the concierge gave Jan a hiking map at 2:30 and several people saw him leave.

Special attention should be paid to Gordon Armgaard. Although the Dutchman said on Thursday that he had to drive to Lisbon to catch a flight, a red Renault, similar to his rental car, was seen hidden behind rocks between Thursday and Saturday. This was only a kilometer or so from the spot where the body was eventually found.

One last oddity. Why was Jan deWys wearing sunglasses on a rainy afternoon?

Suicide Incorporated

A few confusing points. For instance, Godenov seemed to know how he'd been poisoned and what the antidote was, things the average citizen wouldn't know. And the letter setting up the appointment: According to police, it was found in a bottom drawer, in a blank, *sealed* envelope. Godenov's last recorded words also seem a little odd. He refers to the woman as conniving and sneaky, hardly a damning accusation from a man facing death.

Since both forged suicide notes were written by the same person, we can assume that there is only one killer.

As for the coffee, the full cup had probably been poured by the cleaning lady and therefore cannot be taken as evidence of the killer's presence. The lack of prints on the mug could simply mean that the cleaning lady was wearing rubber gloves.

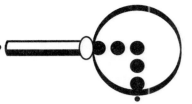

Twice Terminated

The presence of medicine packaging in the garbage is quite significant when linked to the absence of both the bottle and safety seal. Combined with the victim's cold, this points to the liquid medicine as the most likely source of the strychnine. The origin of the tainted medicine is unknown.

Three other facts seem worth noting: The broken locks on Dinsmore's suitcases indicate that the killer may have been looking for something. The horizontal crease on the leather band shows that the watch had been worn by someone with a smaller wrist. The third fact remains unexplained. Why would an expensive watch be sixty-five minutes off the correct time?

But the most puzzling mystery is this: Why would a man undergoing painful symptoms suffer silently instead of using the telephone to seek help?

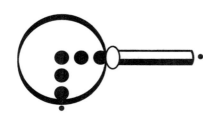

SOLUTIONS

Stories are in alphabetical order.

Attack of the Werewolf

(1) Dr. Ionescu. (2) To retrieve the incriminating diary. (3) The doctor realized that Tim's hemophilia would give him an alibi, if no one else discovered it.

The mystery unraveled when the militia determined that Factor VIII is a blood protein used by hemophiliacs. This was what Tim shared with his maternal grandfather: blood that would not clot. The killer obviously wanted to hide this fact. That was why he mopped up the blood, then went to all the trouble of transporting the corpse to the river and slashing the veins.

Dr. Ionescu had been Werner Havardi's partner in crime, engineering the theft of Communist party funds. When Werner began to be plagued by his conscience and seemed on the verge of confessing, Ionescu felt he had no option but murder. The doctor got away with this crime, too, until Werner's diary made an unexpected appearance in Tim's hands. The odds were good that Werner had left a record of his sins.

After leaving the tavern, Dr. Ionescu went to the Havardi cottage and tried to retrieve the diary. Tim became suspicious and Ionescu was once again forced into murder. The rain hadn't yet started, thereby accounting for the lack of footprints.

Later on, when he and the mayor examined the body, Ionescu was delighted to find his victim's blood still liquid, leading everyone to assume the murder had just been committed. Suddenly he had an alibi. The only challenge remaining was to keep everyone else from discovering Tim's hemophilia.

During the night, the doctor returned to the unlocked cottage. He dragged the body to the waterfall, trying to get rid of as much blood as possible. If there was no sign of Tim's unusual blood, the police would not think of sending off samples for testing. His one mistake was not checking Tim's toiletries for an emergency supply of Factor VIII.

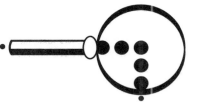

The Baffling Break-ins

(1) The Reverend Billy's accomplice. (2) Billy mailed in a confession. His accomplice broke in to recover it. (3) Break-ins occurred only after mail deliveries.

Eventually, the answer dawned on Chief Atkins. The intruder had been after a piece of mail. That's why the break-ins happened when they did and why his house was not broken into on Sunday.

Armed with this theory, Chief Atkins pieced together a plausible scenario. On Wednesday night, the last night before his disappearance, the Reverend Billy Green telephoned his partner in the church robbery. Green revealed his determination to mail his complete confession to Chief Atkins's home. He then planned to run away. To escape arrest, the accomplice knew he had to intercept the letter before Chief Atkins got his hands on it.

The earliest possible day for the letter's arrival was Friday. For three days, the accomplice lay in wait, watching for the Eucalyptus Lane mail delivery. Each day, after the postman vanished around the corner of Currie Street, the accomplice broke into the house, staying just long enough to check the freshly delivered mail. On Monday morning, the Reverend's letter finally arrived and the accomplice retrieved it from the entryway floor.

Postscript: The Reverend Billy Green was apprehended two months later in Alice Springs. He readily confessed and named his accomplice, the Second Baptist Church's choir director.

The Bee All and End All

(1) Ace Purdy. (2) With formic acid in a syringe. (3) At the hospital as Lord Purdy was recovering from a bee sting.

There is only one theory that adequately reconciles the honey, the two punctures, and the groundskeeper's testimony.

The killer first tried the natural method, spreading honey on the hammock bottom and hoping Lord Purdy would get stung. He did get stung and it was merely coincidence that Beatrice happened to be with him.

Later, in the hospital, when Lord Purdy refused to die, the killer switched to Plan B. Left alone at the old man's bedside, the killer pulled out a syringe previously stolen from Beatrice's medical bag and in-

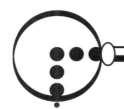

jected him, trusting that the second puncture site would simply blend in with the first.

The murder might have gone undetected, but the family doctor grew suspicious and ordered an autopsy. Bea became the most logical person to take the fall. After all, she was the one who'd been at the hammock. And it was her syringe. On returning to the estate, the killer hid her syringe in a spot where it was bound to be discovered.

According to this, only one of the cousins could be guilty. Only Ace had both gone to the hospital and returned to the estate before the syringe was found.

The Day of the Dead

(1) Hugo. (2) Self-defense and to prevent arrest; either is acceptable. (3)The frugal Maria did not buy fish for Hugo's Saturday dinner, expecting him to be dead by then.

Exactly one year earlier, fate caught up with Pepe Monteneras. Hugo had discovered that his wife, Yolanda, had been having an affair with the over-sexed Pepe. The jealous husband waylaid the drunken Pepe on the footbridge, pushing him to his death.

From the very beginning, Maria suspected murder. But it was a few weeks later, when she found the strange torn-off button wedged in a rock where her husband had fallen, that she hired her private eyes. It took months of investigation, but they finally traced the button to a hand-made jacket Hugo had bought six years before in Acapulco.

Maria had her killer. And he had to pay for his crime in the same way Pepe paid. On the anniversary of Pepe's death, she would lure Hugo to the bridge, then push him through the carefully sawed railing. The mannequin would provide Maria with an alibi. She would sneak back into the cottage by 1:30 at the latest. Everyone would swear she had been in there, working on her book.

But Maria's plan backfired. Hugo was suspicious. As soon as she attacked, he overpowered her, propelling her into the dry riverbed instead.

Maria's lifelong habits of thrift came to her aid after death. She had not expected Hugo to be alive to eat Saturday's dinner. So, there was no reason to buy a good piece of fish that would just go uneaten.

Death of a Dummy

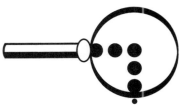

(1) Paterno, Gleason's best friend. (2) By poisoning the cherry on top of the cake. (3) The sticky cards on the table.

Years ago, Paterno (born Yuri Patrenko) was planted in the CIA. It was arranged for him to have a fellow KGB mole as his examining physician. In this way, Paterno's telltale vaccination scars and dental work went unreported.

Though the Cold War was over, Paterno still worked for Russia. Gleason, who had seen Paterno half-naked on various beaches, was about to be briefed on the details of such marks and would have connected this information to his friend.

Paterno brought the cyanide, knowing that Gleason was famous for picking at food, especially desserts. When Paterno saw the candied cherry, he knew Gleason wouldn't be able to resist. During his turn as dummy, Paterno filled the pitted fruit with several grains of poison, then replaced it on the marshmallow icing. Paterno's hands were now sticky from the cherry and the icing, but there was no water to wash his fingers. He certainly couldn't lick them. So, he wiped them off as best he could on a dish towel.

When Gleason filched the cherry during his last kitchen visit, he smoothed over the icing with his fingers, leaving no trace of the cherry, then licked his fingers clean.

During their last full hand, Paterno's sticky hands gummed up the cards, leading Gleason to break out a new deck. Paterno was shuffling this new deck when Gleason collapsed. No one else had touched the deck and yet it also proved to be sticky, just like the old one.

The CIA pieced together this scenario and removed Agent Paterno from Prague. His name soon disappeared from their list of active agents.

Death of the Salesmen
(1) Joël Chirac and Nathaniel Sims were the same person. (2) Annette Chirac. (3) The man's hunting jacket, which Annette was wearing after the murder.

Two and a half years ago, on a business trip, Nathaniel met Annette. At the time, Nathaniel's toupee was being restyled, and he wasn't wearing his contact lenses. Being a married man, Nathaniel gave Annette a false name, Joël Chirac, just to be safe.

Nathaniel fell in love. But he had no intention of divorcing Betty

and losing his sons. So, he created a second life. As Joël Chirac, he found work with a rival drug company. Being his own competition, Nathaniel could manage both jobs, spending half his time with Betty and the other half with Annette, dressing differently, wearing his toupee and covering up his scar with a temporary tattoo. The only thing that remained constant was his tan Pontiac.

But the double life grew exhausting. Nathaniel's best way out was to fake Joël's death, leaving Annette with a rich settlement. He sent the death threats and made the whispering phone call. Using his nose-bleed to supply the blood, Nathaniel then set the scene, knowing the schoolgirl would discover his "corpse" and run off for help.

Nathaniel's troubles began when the police traced his fingerprints. They escalated when Annette recognized him in the lineup. She waited for him outside the police station, then trailed him home. A short time later, when Nathaniel drove off on his hunting trip, she followed.

Annette stabbed him with a second steak knife from her kitchen and blood spurted all over her green jacket. It would have been too dangerous to drive the 150 kilometers home with a bloody jacket. So, Annette burned her own jacket in the campfire and took Nathaniel's, driving to work just in time for her shift.

The police deduced that a hunter would not be wearing a green jacket and that the oversized red jacket Annette wore had the buttons on the right, an indication that it was a man's style.

Death Takes a Ski Weekend
(1) Boris Stuttgart, her husband. (2) He laid out Paulina's body with the wig, killing Belle later. (3) Jealousy over Belle's infidelity.

Belle Stuttgart and Hansel Aroma had been having an affair. Boris discovered this and carefully bided his time, waiting for just the right opportunity. That opportunity came with Paulina's heart attack. The fact that the women were fairly similar in build and age gave him his inspiration.

Boris forged a love note from Hansel, knowing that Belle would rush off at six o'clock to the caretaker's cottage. He also knew that Hansel's conference call would keep the lovers from bumping into each other during that critical period.

Before going to the lounge, Boris used the terrace to move Paulina's

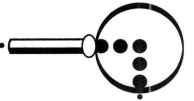

body from one guest room to the other, covering up her gym outfit with the silk robe and one of Belle's distinctive wigs. When he brought the two witnesses back to his room, they naturally assumed this "strangled" corpse was Belle's.

While Boris was supposedly off by himself mourning, he walked out to the cottage, where he surprised his wife who was still waiting for Hansel. Belle tried to cover up her guilt and willingly accompanied him back to their bedroom. Belle was astonished by the sight of the blond corpse and Boris seized his chance, strangling her from behind. During Belle's brief struggle, the note fell from her pocket.

Then came the cleanup. He undressed his wife. Then he removed the robe and wig from the cold corpse, placing them on the fresh corpse and arranging the body in the same position. Finally, he carried Paulina's corpse back across the terrace to the other guest room. Everyone would believe that Belle was dead a good fifteen minutes before she actually was, thereby giving Boris his alibi.

The Judge's Judgment Day
(1) Ernesto, the bodyguard. (2) The gunshot sounds were on the Vivaldi tape. Ernesto shot the drugged judge before letting anyone into the room. (3) A paid Mafia assassination.

The Mafia had to make an example of Judge Sentini. A simple poisoning or a simple shooting would not inspire half the fear that an impossible, phantom murder would. Ernesto was paid a lot of money to arrange it, and all he needed from his employers was a duplicate of the judge's favorite Vivaldi tape, one with the sound of three gunshots placed strategically in the middle section.

Ernesto had keys to the office. It was very easy for him to enter one evening and replace the judge's morning tape with the "gunshot" one. The next morning, while preparing the breakfast tray, Ernesto drugged the coffee pot, then left to find himself an alibi witness in the garden.

As always, the judge followed Ernesto's instructions, locking the door and leaving the key in the lock. He drank his coffee and turned on his music, all part of his unvarying routine. When the gunshots sounded on the tape, Judge Sentini was already partly paralyzed from the diazepam. He cried out in alarm and got up to check the stereo. Then he collapsed, dragging himself partway across the floor.

When Ernesto broke the terrace window, he counted on the alarm

to cover up the sound of the real murder. He screwed a silencer onto the muzzle of his semiautomatic, killed his boss, then unlocked the door to admit the rest of the household.

The assassin knew it would take at least thirty minutes before the Naples police arrived. This gave him enough time to reenter the study and replace the gunshot tape with the original. This was an especially easy job since he himself was assigned to guard the room.

The Marquis de Sade's Locked Room
(1) Georges de Sade. (2) Georges de Sade. (3) After the supposed theft, when Georges searched the inner room

The idea to steal occurred to Georges that Thursday morning when he and his family first saw the Napoleon letter. The naturally greedy son knew he could never persuade his father to sell a de Sade document. Stealing was the only way.

Georges set the scene by slipping the packet of money under the professor's door Friday night. On Sunday afternoon, he disguised himself with the wig and beard and rented the room, making sure to choose a seedy hotel where there was no night clerk. Then late Sunday night, Georges knocked on the professor's door. Making up some story about additional de Sade papers, Georges lured Professor Petit to the hotel room, where he proceeded to strangle him to death.

On Monday, when the professor didn't show up at the bank, Georges was ready. He bullied his way into the vault's inner room and pretended to find the professor's business card. Then, when the guard left to call the police, Georges had plenty of time to find the Napoleon letter and slip it into his clothing, leaving the dead professor to take credit for an impossible theft.

The Masked Phantom
(1) Fernando Fernas. (2) In the first attack, he lied about the masked killer. In the second, he taped open the fire exit. (3) The first motive was robbery; the second was to give credence to his masked-killer story.

It was Fernando's first attempt at armed robbery and it went horribly wrong, resulting in Carmen Neves's death. As the out-of-work laborer knelt over his victim to take her jewelry and purse, he was caught by two witnesses. Thinking quickly, he made up a story about a masked

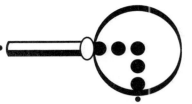

killer. While the witnesses were off in the side alley, Fernando ran out to Rua Mariana and disposed of the gun in a garbage sack.

What Fernando didn't know at the time was that the side alley was a dead end. This naturally made him the prime suspect. The only thing preventing the police from an arrest was the lack of a gun. Once they found it and connected it to the Rua Mariana garbage, he would be exposed.

In order to bolster his story, Fernando needed to create a masked killer and to have this killer disappear in front of witnesses. When the police showed him the usher's testimony, they inadvertently gave him the timetable he needed.

Fernando entered the movie theater for an earlier show, taping open the latch to the fire-exit door. Then, a few minutes after midnight, he put on his wig, beard, and mask and hid in the alley. On the first night, nothing happened. No lone pedestrian walked through the alley during the critical period of time.

On the second night, Fernando got lucky. At 12:20, the phantom killer made himself seen by a witness, waved a gun, then disappeared into the dead-end alley. Once inside the auditorium, Fernando joined the crowd of incoming customers and took a seat. Soon after the movie started, he walked out, disposing of his disguise and a second gun in a public men's room.

River of No Return

(1) Margo and Gordon Armgaard. (2) Fraud. (3) Margo and Gordon killed Jan on Thursday, then had Gordon impersonate him at the new hotel.

The police would never have investigated a casual acquaintance like Gordon Armgaard had it not been for the sighting of the red Renault. They checked with the rental agency and the airlines, then questioned Gordon. He eventually confessed.

"Margo and I had been defrauding the deWys trust. When deWys grew suspicious, Margo arranged this hiking trip. The plot was all her idea. She needed an alibi and no one was even supposed to suspect me.

"We killed him Thursday on our hike, planting his body between the river rocks. You could never see it from the path. Then I put on an identical outfit and hiked back to the hotel, pretending to be deWys.

That night I laid low in the room. The next morning I sneaked out to the car while Margo paid the bill. Sophia almost caught up with us, but we managed to avoid her.

"At the Vimioso hotel, no one knew the real deWys. Still, I played things safe with the sunglasses. Sophia was waiting to ambush deWys as he left. Being his wife, she knew exactly what he looked like and didn't give me a second glance.

"I planted deWys's gear on the cliff. Then I hiked along the riverbank down to the spot where we'd hidden the Renault. That same night I flew back home to Amsterdam. When the police found the body, we thought they'd assume the obvious. A lone hiker fell off a cliff and got washed downstream. Who knew the Portuguese police could be so efficient?"

Suicide Incorporated

(1) Robert Godenov. (2) Godenov, with some unwitting help from the cleaning lady. (3) The cleaning lady had found Godenov's sweetener packet containing cyanide.

A private detective working for the defense recovered the contents of the trash can by the coffee counter. In a discarded sweetener packet, he found a single grain of potassium cyanide, which wound up solving the case.

It was the second victim, Robert Godenov, who had schemed so lethally for the leadership of Yungun Best Advertising. After George Yungun died from a heart attack, Godenov murdered his replacement, Keith Best, making it look like suicide. Then, when Betina Anderson threatened to become the next CEO, Godenov plotted a second "suicide." Not only would Betina die, but in doing so, she would take the blame for the first murder.

Bob Godenov came into the office that evening to put the finishing touches on his plan. Tomorrow morning, he would give the sealed letter to Betina; tomorrow evening he would kill her. He had worked hard to make the suicide note resemble Betina's handwriting, though he was still practicing her signature. He had also stored up a precious cache of cyanide, hiding it in an artificial sweetener packet in one of his drawers.

But the cleaning lady ruined his well-laid plans. She rummaged around, found his "sweet" cyanide and was about to use it in her coffee when she was interrupted. Godenov went for his own cup of java, us-

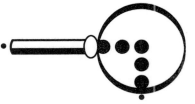

ing the opened sweetener packet on the counter. He didn't suspect it was his own poison packet.

Godenov took a deep gulp of coffee and instantly knew. He cursed the cleaning lady, called security, then went in search of an antidote. Too late.

Twice Terminated

(1) James O'Connor. (2) He poisoned the cold medicine which Paddy Dinsmore then stole from his room. (3) It was a mistake; O'Connor had intended to poison his wife.

Why was the watch sixty-five minutes fast? Because it was still set on Paris time. It was James O'Connor's property, as were the diamond ring, much of the cash, and the fatal bottle of medicine. But let's start at the beginning.

O'Connor wanted to kill his wife. The reason's not important. Suffice it to say, she owned the estate and controlled much of their wealth, and he wanted out.

O'Connor bought the cold medicine, and while in his bedroom, he poisoned it. He was hoping to lay the blame on an act of consumer terrorism. But while he was off doing laps, the fired groundskeeper broke in, stole his watch, money, ring, and, since he had a cold, the repackaged medicine. This explains why Dinsmore didn't seek help. To do so would be to turn himself in as a thief. Better to tough it out and hope it was just indigestion.

When O'Connor discovered Dinsmore in his final spasms, he realized that the wrong person had gotten hold of the poison. Had he done nothing, he might have gotten away with it. But the businessman panicked. He grabbed the key, opened the trunk, retrieved the leftover medicine from Dinsmore's suitcase, and disposed of it. Then he returned to the house and called the police.

Later in the investigation, the police showed Mr. O'Connor the suspiciously expensive watch and ring. He denied ownership. But Mrs. O'Connor quickly identified both items, leading to her husband's arrest.

Oh, and why was the expensive watch sixty-five minutes off instead of exactly an hour? Like many busy people, O'Connor purposely kept his watch five minutes fast so that he wouldn't miss appointments.

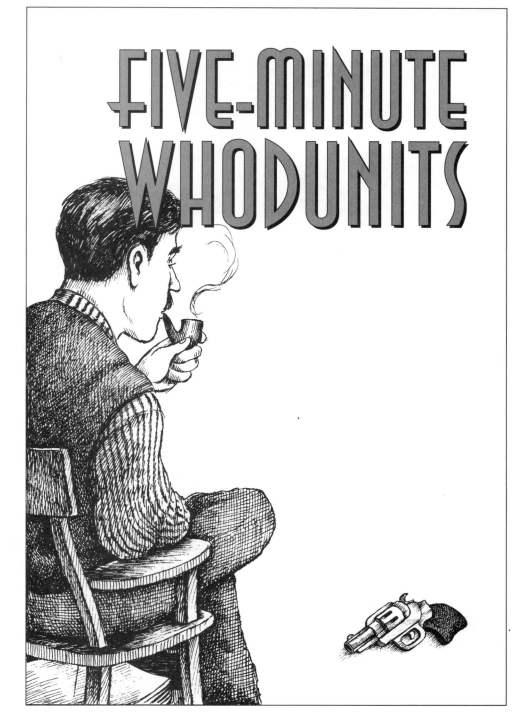

FIVE-MINUTE WHODUNITS

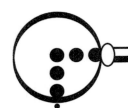

MR. THOMAS P. STANWICK

Even those unacquainted with Thomas P. Stanwick are often struck by his appearance. A lean and lanky young man, he stands six feet two inches tall. His long, thin face is complemented by a full head of brown hair and a droopy mustache. Though not husky in build, he is surprisingly strong and enjoys ruggedly good health.

His origins and early life are obscure. He is undeniably well educated, however, for he graduated with high honors from Dartmouth College as a philosophy major and studied logic and history at Cambridge University for a year or two afterwards. He now lives alone (with a pet Labrador) in a bungalow in the New England town of Baskerville, not far from the city of Royston. His house is filled with books, chess sets, maps, and charts. He earns a living as a freelance editor of textbooks on geometry and American history.

Personally, Stanwick is good-humored and amiable. His relaxed manner conceals the strength of his convictions and the intensity of his intellectual interests. He enjoys the company of his many friends, but cherishes his personal freedom and independence. The regular patterns of his life suit him well, and the pursuit of wealth, fame, or power holds no attraction for him.

His main interests are his intellectual pursuits. First and foremost, he is a logician, particularly skilled in traditional formal deduction. As an incessant student of its theoretical and practical aspects, he is fascinated by all sorts of mysteries and puzzles. Aside from pure logic, other

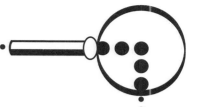

interests of his include philosophy, chess, history, music, mathematics, literature, and etymology. An avid bibliophile, he owns hundreds of books on those topics.

Stanwick's personal tastes are simple. A casual dresser, he almost never wears a tie. His eating preferences are old-fashioned and include beef and potatoes. An ardent Anglophile, he has several British habits acquired during his many long stays in England. He prefers tea to coffee, for example, and smokes a pipe.

Besides seeing his friends, Stanwick's favorite pastimes are reading and chess. He is also fond of hiking in the New England hills. He takes long travel vacations in the summertime and often visits England. Sometimes he stays with the Earl of Stanwyck, a distant relative, at the earl's East Anglian estate or at his country estate in Scotland. He also enjoys visiting London and Cambridge, where he has many friends from his student days. Back home in Baskerville, he carries on an active correspondence.

He spends many of his evenings conversing with friends at the Royston Chess Club and elsewhere. When he has a hand in investigating and solving crimes, it is usually through his friendship with Inspector Matt Walker, a promising detective on the Royston police force who is about five years older than Stanwick. They play chess together at the chess club on Thursday evenings, and Stanwick occasionally drops by police headquarters.

Stanwick's interest in criminal cases is purely that of a logician. In that capacity, as Walker would be the first to admit, he is frequently very useful.

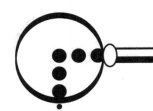

THE CASE OF THE WELLS FARGO MONEY

The daring theft of half a million dollars from a Wells Fargo armored truck captured the imagination of the entire Royston area. As the *Royston Gazette* excitedly summarized it, the truck had just been loaded with cash from the First National Bank on the afternoon of June 4 when two or three men appeared, overpowered the guards, piled the money into a pickup truck, and disappeared—all in less than five minutes.

The investigation was placed in the hands of Inspector Matthew Walker. His skillful inquiries led the police to three men who often worked together and were suspected of several lesser robberies.

Some 10 miles from the city, in the little town of Baskerville, Thomas P. Stanwick, the amateur logician, pushed aside a postal chess analysis and admitted the inspector to his bungalow.

"I'm delighted to see you, Matt," said Stanwick as they seated themselves in the living room. "I hear you've been doing fine work on this Wells Fargo case."

"Thanks, Tom." Walker smiled wearily. "All the public attention has put a lot of pressure on us to solve it and, if possible, recover the money."

"I've also heard you have some suspects under surveillance."

"That's right. This is strictly confidential, of course." Walker leaned forward in his armchair. "We have conclusive evidence that Charles Acker, Bull Barrington, and Adam Crowley organized the job, and at least two of them actually carried it out. We've been monitoring their communications, hoping to get more information. The money has been hidden, and not all three of them know where it is. It would aid us enormously to find out who knows its location.

"To complicate matters, at least one of them communicates by a 'lying code', in which everything he says is false. The others speak truthfully. We don't know which, or how many of them, are using the lying code."

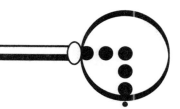

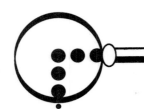

Stanwick idly twisted the tip of his mustache and chuckled. "Quite a problem. Can I help?"

"I hope so." Walker flipped open his notebook. "These are the only helpful statements we've been able to intercept that might tell us who's lying and who knows where the money is:

Acker: Barrington is using the lying code, and I know where the money is.

Barrington : Acker was out of town at the time of the robbery.

Crowley: Acker was in town at the time of the robbery if and only if he knows where the money is.

Barrington: I don't use the lying code.

Acker: Either I was in town at the time of the robbery or Crowley does not use the lying code.

Crowley: Not all of us use the lying code. I don't know where the money is.

"As you can see, it's a bit of a tangle," Walker concluded.

Stanwick took and studied the notebook for a few minutes, and then handed it back.

"My dinner's almost ready," he said, standing up. "Pot roast, potatoes, and peas. Since you'll be working late anyway, I hope you can stay long enough to join me. In the meantime, I'll be glad to tell you who is lying, and at least one man who knows where the money is."

Who is lying? Who knows where the money is?

Solution on page 155

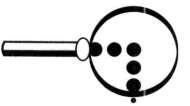

A SLAYING
IN THE NORTH END

"Well, Matt, what big-city crimes are testing the skills and trying the patience of Royston's finest this week?"

Thomas P. Stanwick, the amateur logician, grinned at Inspector Walker as he dropped into the visitor's chair of the inspector's chronically cluttered office. Stretching his long legs toward the desk, he fumbled for his pipe.

Walker looked up wearily.

"Good to see you, Tom. I thought you were all tied up with that geometry textbook revision."

"That should be finished by Friday," replied Stanwick, lighting his briar. "By next Wednesday, I'll be off to London and Cambridge for two weeks of loitering, puttering in musty bookshops, and reminiscing about student days. What's up, though? You look frazzled."

"I sure am." Walker pawed through a pile of papers on his desk and pulled out four. "These are my notes on the Minot Street shooting. I've been up all night compiling them. There are still several gangs fighting up there in the North End. Les Chaven, the leader of the Blackhawks, was shot and killed last Friday afternoon by a member of the Leopards, apparently in a turf fight over Minot Street."

"So both gangs love Minot, eh?" said Stanwick.

Walker winced. "The members of the Leopard gang," the inspector continued, "are Al Foster, Bruce Diskin, Charlie Jensen, Damon O'Keefe, and Eddie Lyons. Their gang is pretty new, so we don't know yet which is the leader. Nor do we know which is the killer. So far, all I've been able to dig up are these facts:

"1. The killer and the leader had a fierce argument about whether to kill Chaven before deciding to go ahead with it.

"2. Jensen works the evening shift as a machinist in the local plant on weeknights and is thinking of working at his brother's gym-bag factory in San Francisco.

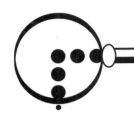

"3. The leader's wife is a teller at the Second National Bank. Foster, an only child, works part-time as a janitor there.

"4. The leader and Diskin play poker every Tuesday night at eight over Hiller's Saloon. Foster picks them up there after midnight and drives them home.

"5. Jensen is married to the killer's sister, who was once engaged to O'Keefe.

"6. O'Keefe, a bachelor, is the best lockpick of the five."

Stanwick, fingering the tip of his mustache, quietly glanced over Walker's notes and then handed them back. An amused twinkle lit his eye as he watched Walker give a gaping yawn.

"What you need," he said, "is a little more sleep. If you weren't so tired, I'm sure you'd see that there's easily enough information here to deduce the identities of both the leader and the killer."

Who is the leader? Who is the killer?

Solution on page 155

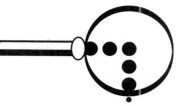

BAD DAY FOR BERNIDI

During a midday visit to the city of Royston, Thomas P. Stanwick, the amateur logician, noticed several police cars at the entrance of Bernidi's, a small downtown jewelry store. Toying with the tip of his mustache in thoughtful curiosity, he approached and eased his way through a knot of onlookers. His friend Inspector Matt Walker was inside, and he signaled to the policeman at the door to let Stanwick in.

"Hello, Tom," exclaimed Walker in mild surprise. "What brings you here?"

"I was just passing by," replied Stanwick. He glanced around the cool, dark interior of the narrow room. "What happened?"

"I was just about to ask Mr. Bernidi to repeat his story to me."

The two turned to the small, white-haired owner, who was leaning against one of the two display counters that ran the length of both sides of the room. His face was streaked with dust, and he looked exhausted.

"I had just stepped into the back," he said, "when I hear the bell on the front door ring. I come out, and there's this guy, very well dressed, looking around and coming toward me and the register. 'Can I help you?' I say, and he smiles and pulls a gun halfway out of his jacket pocket. A little piece, but I can see it's real. Then he puts it back, but keeps his hand in there. There's nobody else around, so what can I do?

"Anyway, he makes me open the register, but I just made a deposit, so there's only a few bucks. He doesn't get mad, but takes a piece of clothesline out of another pocket, ties my hands behind my back, and makes me lie down on my stomach behind the side counter here, with my face to the wall.

"It was tight; you can see there's not much room back there. Then I hear him opening the wood panels—these here, the lower half of the counter—but he finds nothing. I only keep supplies down there. Then he steps across to the opposite counter, pulls out a little burlap sack, smashes the glass, scoops some rings into the sack, and runs out. I get up, see the broken glass, and yell for a cop."

"What did the man look like?" asked Walker.

"Like I told the officer—big, burly guy, clean-shaven, dark hair."

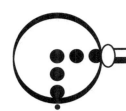

"Don't you have your display glass wired to an alarm?" inquired Stanwick.

"Never got around to it. It's insured, anyway."

"Well, thank you, Mr. Bernidi," said Walker, closing his notebook. "We'll check around and let you know when we make an arrest."

"I think you can make an arrest right now," said Stanwick quietly.

Whom does Stanwick suspect, and why?

Solution on page 149

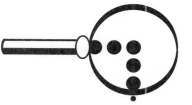

AN UNACCOUNTABLE DEATH

On this rainy Tuesday, as on many other Tuesdays around noon, Thomas P. Stanwick, the amateur logician, called on his friend Inspector Matt Walker in the inspector's tiny, cluttered office in Royston. Walker usually had a case or two on hand that he knew would pique the interest and exercise the particular talents of his friend. This day was no exception.

"We've got a shooting death on our hands, Tom," said Walker, leaning back in his chair. "Herb Lombard, the manager of a small accounting firm in the Cummins Building, was found dead at his desk late yesterday afternoon. He may have shot himself, but we're not sure."

Stanwick idly fingered the tip of his mustache.

"Who discovered the body?" he asked.

"A client of his named John Morey, who works in another office down the hall. Lombard was working on some late personal tax returns for him. Morey says he was leaving work yesterday, shortly after five, when he passed the door of Lombard's firm and decided to see if Lombard was in. The clerks had already left the outer office, but light was shining from under the door of Lombard's inner office.

"Morey knocked, opened the door, and found Lombard slumped over his desk in a puddle of blood with a revolver in his hand. Morey was so scared that, without touching anything in the room, he ran down to a pay phone in the lobby and called headquarters.

"I arrived a few minutes later and accompanied him back to Lombard's inner office. Snapping on the light, I found everything just as Morey had described. Lombard had been dead for less than an hour, and had a bullet wound in his head. The revolver had been fired once."

Stanwick shifted slightly in his chair.

"Poor devil," he remarked. "Did Morey find the door to the outer office open?"

"No, but it had been left unlocked," replied Walker.

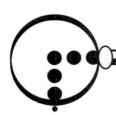

"I see." Stanwick looked grim. "You'd better arrest Morey at once, Matt. He's lying about this affair!"

Why does Stanwick suspect Morey?

Solution on page 155

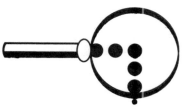

THE CASE OF THE PURLOINED PAINTING

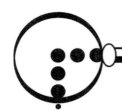

There were times, thought Thomas P. Stanwick, when you could never count on having a friendly conversation without an interruption. Especially if your friend was a police inspector and you were visiting his office when a robbery call came in.

The amateur logician and Inspector Walker pulled up in front of a large brick house in a wealthy neighborhood in Royston and were quickly shown into the living room. A valuable painting had been stolen from the wall. The thief had apparently broken the glass in a nearby patio door, let himself in, and left by the same route. An obviously shaken maid was sitting in a large armchair when Stanwick and Walker entered.

"She discovered the theft and called it in, sir," a uniformed officer told Walker. "The couple who live here are out of town this week."

"What happened?" Walker asked the maid.

"I didn't hear a thing," she replied. "I had been working in the kitchen and was on my way to my room. When I passed the living room, I noticed that the painting was gone and that the glass in the patio door was broken. I called the police right away."

Stanwick carefully opened the patio door and walked out onto the concrete patio, stepping gingerly around the long shards of broken glass there as well as around any possible footmarks. He observed faint smudges of mud under the glass.

"How long had the painting hung in here?" he asked as he came back in.

"About two years, I guess," answered the maid.

Stanwick sat down in a comfortable armchair, crossed his legs, and turned to Walker.

"Well, Matt," he said, "I think you may want to ask this lady some more questions. This job involved inside help!"

Why is Stanwick sure that inside help was involved?

Solution on page 156

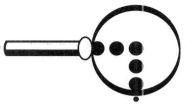

THE WEEK OF THE QUEEN ANNE FESTIVAL

Ah, to be in England, now that summer's here, thought Thomas P. Stanwick as he descended to the pub for breakfast. He was beginning a two-month vacation in England with a week's stay at the Grey Boar Inn, a few miles outside Knordwyn.

The amateur logician had first visited Knordwyn, a tiny village in Northumbria, a year earlier, and had become very fond of it and greatly intrigued by its peculiarities. Chief among these was that about half the villagers always told the truth, and the rest always lied. Stanwick thus found his conversations there wonderful challenges for his powers of deduction.

It was a beautiful Monday morning, and Stanwick gathered his thoughts over a hearty breakfast of eggs, bacon, toast, and tea. He knew that this was the week of the Queen Anne Festival, held annually in Knordwyn since Queen Anne stopped overnight in the village on her way to visit Scotland in 1702. People gathered on festival days from many surrounding towns to enjoy dancing, balladeering, cooking, racing, and other activities.

The trouble was that the festival date and the number of festival days varied from year to year, and Stanwick wasn't sure which days this year were the festival days. He knew that today was not a festival day, and that the festival would be over before Saturday. At least one, and possibly more, of the intervening days would be festival days, and he wanted to know precisely which.

Finishing his breakfast, Stanwick lit his pipe, leaned back in his chair, and idly fingered a tip of his brown mustache as he looked slowly around the room. The other tables were empty except for one by a large window. Around that table were gathered three grizzled villagers, all cronies of the innkeeper, nursing early mugs of ale. Stanwick had seen them before and knew that their names were Chiswick, Green, and Hunter, but he didn't know which were liars and which were truth-

tellers. Well, he thought, perhaps today he would find out.

Stanwick arose and strolled over to their table.

"Good morning, gentlemen," he said cheerfully. "I beg your pardon, but could you please tell me which days this week are festival days? Also, if you'll excuse my asking, which of you are liars?"

The three villagers glanced at each other silently for a moment. Chiswick was the first to speak.

"We are all liars," said he, "and Friday is a festival day."

"He speaks the truth," Green said. "Also, Tuesday is a festival day."

Hunter took a gulp from his mug.

"If Chiswick is lying," he said as he set it down, "then Green is telling the truth. Also, Wednesday is a festival day."

"Thank you, gentlemen," said Stanwick, who turned and walked off with a delighted smile. He now knew which of the three were liars and which days that week were festival days.

Who is lying?
Which days are festival days?

Solution on page 156

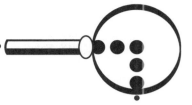

DEATH OF A CON MAN

Thomas P. Stanwick was engrossed in revising some notes at his desk late one spring afternoon when the doorbell rang. He opened the door and found Inspector Walker standing on the step.

"Matt! Come in," Stanwick exclaimed, stepping aside. "It's nice of you to drop by on your way back to Royston."

Walker looked surprised.

"How did you know which direction I came from?" he asked. "I parked in the driveway, not on the street."

"Quite so, but I observe that the small mud patch by the driveway entrance on the side toward Royston is undisturbed. Had you come from Royston, you could hardly have avoided at least grazing it as you turned in."

Walker laughed as they settled themselves into a pair of comfortable armchairs in the living room.

"Never expect to keep secrets when you visit a logician," he said. "I'm on my way back from Richford, where I've been following up some leads on the Edmunds murder last week."

"Edmunds? Isn't he the con man who was shot in a shipping warehouse?" asked Stanwick as he relit his pipe.

"That's right. We've arrested four members of a gang he recently fleeced: Cannon, Cochran, Carruthers, and Carpenter. We know one of them is the killer. Our polygraph showed that each made one true statement and one false statement this morning under interrogation, but we couldn't determine which was which."

Stanwick leaned forward eagerly. "Do you have a copy of the statements?"

Walker smiled, reached into his coat pocket, and pulled out a folded document.

"I thought you might find them interesting," he said as he handed the paper across. "If you can make any use of them, I'd be glad to hear your conclusions."

Stanwick unfolded the paper, leaned back, and read:

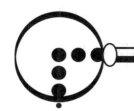

Cannon: I did not kill Edmunds. Carpenter is the killer.

Cochran: I did not kill Edmunds. Cannon is lying when he says Carpenter is the killer.

Carruthers: I did not kill Edmunds. Either Cannon is the killer or none of us is.

Carpenter: I did not kill Edmunds. If Carruthers did not kill Edmunds, then Cannon did.

"At least they were all consistent with their denials," Stanwick said with a laugh. "However, a little deduction is enough to clear up the matter. The killer is…"

Who is the killer?

Solution on page 156

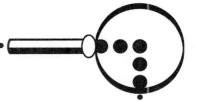

THE CASE OF THE EDGEMORE STREET SHOOTING

"Thanks for coming over, Tom," said Inspector Matt Walker as Thomas P. Stanwick, the amateur logician, strolled into the inspector's office at Royston Police headquarters.

"Glad to," Stanwick replied as he flopped into a chair. "You said you were going to interrogate a suspect in that recent street shooting."

"That's right." Walker lit a cheap cigar. "As you may already know, Bruce Walder, a local businessman in his mid-fifties, was walking along Edgemore Street about dusk two days ago. Someone approached him, shot him in the chest, and ran off. We suspect that the shooter wanted to rob him, and shot him when Walder started to resist.

"We haven't located anyone who actually saw the crime, but several locals were able to describe a man they saw lounging in the street shortly before it took place. Their descriptions matched that of Victor Kravitz, a small-time mugger known to frequent the area. We picked up Kravitz just a few hours ago. Let's hear what he has to say."

They went to a nearby interrogation room. Kravitz, a small, nervous man with thinning blond hair, sat beside his lawyer and chain-smoked. Two detectives leaned against the wall while Walker and Stanwick sat down at the table.

"You've got it all wrong," cried Kravitz. "I didn't shoot Walder. I was on the street earlier, sure, but just hanging around. When I saw some guy come out of an alley, come up behind the stiff, and shoot him, I ran. I didn't want no trouble."

"You saw the crime committed?" asked Walker.

"Yeah. Yeah."

"Why didn't you report it?" asked one of the other detectives.

Kravitz laughed nervously. "Sure. Like you guys were about to believe me."

"Can you describe the man?" Walker inquired.

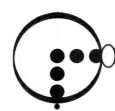

"Sure, sure. Middle-aged guy, tall, red mustache. Wore a big gray overcoat and a hat. Walder never even saw him."

"Where did you run to?"

"My girlfriend's place. You can ask her."

Stanwick, who had been slouching back in his chair, cleared his throat and slowly sat up.

"I for one have heard enough, Matt," he said to Walker. "This man is obviously lying."

How does Stanwick know that Kravitz is lying?

Solution on page 157

108

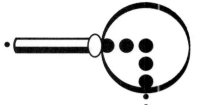

DEATH COMES TO THE COLONEL

Thomas P. Stanwick, the amateur logician, and Inspector Matthew Walker of the Royston Police strode into the richly carpeted study of Jeremy Huddleston. It was a chilly Tuesday in late fall, and Stanwick had been chatting in Walker's office when word came in of Huddleston's sudden death. Poisoning was suspected.

Huddleston, a retired army colonel in his seventies, lay behind his desk in the middle of the room, partly covered by his overturned chair. His sightless eyes stared at the ceiling as a fire crackled in the large brick hearth behind the desk. Near the hearth, a young, balding man sat wearily in an armchair. Walker approached him.

"Mr. Huddleston?" he asked. "Mr. George Huddleston?"

The young man nodded.

"The colonel's grand-nephew, aren't you?"

"Yes."

"Please tell us what happened."

Huddleston looked up nervously and wet his lips. "I came into the study about ten this morning to say good morning to Uncle Jeremy. He was working at his desk and seemed to be in cheerful spirits. He asked me to pour him another cup of coffee from the sideboard, so I did. He drank about half of it, and then suddenly put his cup down and said, 'Before I forget, I must call Phillips to fix the leak in the basement pipes.'"

"Roy Phillips, the local plumber?" Walker cut in.

"That's right." Huddleston continued. "He had just started to dial his private phone when he uttered a sharp cry, clutched suddenly at his throat, and fell over onto the floor. I was horrified and rushed over to him, but could see at once that he was dead.

"Hurrying out to the hall, I locked the study door and called to his housekeeper, Mrs. Stowe, who phoned the doctor and the police. I kept the study door locked until you arrived."

A medical assistant touched Walker on the shoulder.

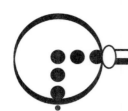

"Excuse me, sir," he said. "The drops we extracted from the coffee cup show definite traces of cyanide."

Walker nodded. Stanwick lit his pipe and looked slowly around the room. His gaze rested in turn on the cheery fire warming the room of death, on the half-empty coffee cup resting neatly in its saucer, and on the West Point ring adorning the victim's finger.

"Do you live here, Mr. Huddleston?" Stanwick asked, suddenly turning to the nephew.

"No," replied Huddleston. "I live in California, where I work for an architecural firm. I was here only for the week, to visit Uncle Jeremy and see the East Coast again."

The phone on the colonel's desk rang. Walker answered it and bluntly told the caller, an old friend of the colonel's nephew, that the colonel was dead and a police investigation was in progress. After hanging up, he faced George Huddleston again.

"What more can you tell us, Mr. Huddleston?" he asked.

"Nothing," replied Huddleston listlessly.

"On the contrary," said Stanwick sharply, "I think Mr. Huddleston could help by telling us the truth."

How does Stanwick know that Huddleston is lying?

Solution on page 157

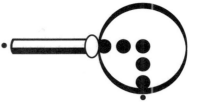

STANWICK FINDS THE
MAGIC WORDS

The small downtown section of Baskerville was unusually busy that Saturday morning. After browsing through several other stores, Thomas P. Stanwick wandered into the Baskerville Bookshop, a crowded, bright little store displaying books, greeting cards and, in a far corner, toys. He was looking for a birthday present for the younger son of his friend Inspector Matt Walker. Tim Walker was about to turn six.

Weaving his way through knots of other customers, Stanwick made his way to the toy corner. There he spotted a toy he knew Tim would love: a bright red fire truck. Scooping it up, Stanwick started for the checkout counter and then stopped with a sudden realization. He had accidentally left his wallet at home.

With a sigh of annoyance, Stanwick turned to put the truck back. As he did, he saw a sign near a collection of puzzle books:

SAY THE MAGIC WORDS!

How sharp are your puzzle skills? Tell us the logical conclusion of the following statements and win the book or toy of your choice!

1. All friends of winged armadillos wear striped ties.

2. Only those who eat pickled harmonicas can enter a chocolate courtroom.

3. Members of the Diagonal Club drink martinis only at four.

4. All who eat pickled harmonicas are friends of winged armadillos.

5. Only those green elephants who are members of the Diagonal Club can wear striped ties.

6. All green elephants drink martinis at five.

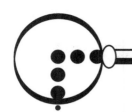

Stanwick's eyes sparkled. For a few moments, he stood stock still, staring at the sign and fingering the tip of his mustache. Then, with a gesture of triumph, he swung the truck back under his arm, strode to the checkout counter, and won the truck for Tim by saying the magic words.

What are the magic words?

Solution on page 157

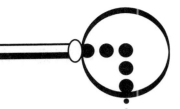

THE GREAT WATERMELON COVER-UP

Thomas P. Stanwick had just stepped into Kreckman's Grocery Store in Baskerville to buy some tea and some pipe tobacco when the owner, Otto Kreckman, hurried up to him anxiously.

"Mr. Stanwick, I'm so glad to see you," he said. "Come see what's happened!"

Kreckman led Stanwick down an aisle of the small shop. At the far end, several large watermelons had been knocked from a display table and lay smashed on the floor. Four ten-year-old boys stood nervously around the pulpy wreckage.

"These boys were fooling around back here," said the grocer angrily, "and one or more of them knocked over my melons. None will admit doing it, though.

"The damage isn't much," he told Stanwick privately in a lower voice, "but whoever is guilty should learn some responsibility."

Stanwick, affecting a cold stare, silently looked from one boy to the next as he slowly filled and lit his pipe. They all lived in Baskerville, and he knew their names.

"Richard," he asked abruptly, "who knocked over those melons?"

"Harry and Frank knocked them over," Richard replied.

Harry and Frank angrily turned to him.

"I didn't knock them over!" said Frank hotly.

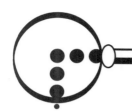

Stanwick turned to the redheaded boy. "What do you have to say, Tommy?"

Tommy fidgeted uncomfortably. "Only one of us knocked the melons over."

"How about you, Harry?"

"What Tommy and Frank said is true," Harry replied sullenly.

Kreckman took Stanwick aside.

"They won't tell me any more than that," said the grocer. "Now, I know these boys. Tommy's an honest kid, and I'm sure he wouldn't lie to me. He's too loyal to his friends to tell me who's responsible, though.

"Harry, on the other hand, is a different sort altogether and lies his head off anytime he's suspected of mischief. As for the others, I don't know whom to believe, and I can't pinpoint the culprits."

"In that case," said Stanwick with a sly smile, "I can be of some help. I know exactly who is responsible."

Who knocked over the watermelons?

Solution on page 157

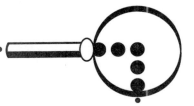

INSPECTOR WALKER FEELS THE HEAT

"Hello, Tom? Matt here. Have you got a few minutes to spare this afternoon? We're really up against it here, and I could use some advice. Mind if I come right over? Thanks."

As Thomas P. Stanwick hung up the phone, he reflected that his friend Inspector Walker, who had just called from police headquarters, sounded unusually tense and anxious. A few prominent citizens of the city of Royston had been assaulted recently, and Stanwick wondered if one of those cases might be troubling Walker.

Within half an hour, the inspector had driven out from Royston and arrived at Stanwick's bungalow in Baskerville. The amateur logician promptly ushered him into the living room, where they sat down.

"You look pretty harried, Matt," observed Stanwick as he filled his pipe. "What's up?"

"It's the attack on the deputy mayor two nights ago," Walker replied.

"Ah, yes. I remember reading something about it in the paper. Beaten and robbed as he walked home after attending a late neighborhood committee meeting, I think."

"That's right. He wasn't very badly hurt, but is still in the hospital. The night was so dark, and the attack so sudden, that he isn't sure whether he was attacked by one man or several. The mayor has ordered an all-out investigation, and has really turned on the pressure."

Stanwick grinned faintly. "I can imagine."

"Our search," continued Walker, "has narrowed down to five men. One is Robert Ellis, a small-time mugger. The other four are a gang of ruffians from the north end of the city. Their names are Al Chase, Archie Heath, Dick Mullaney, and Bull Decker. At least one of the five is guilty."

"What can you tell me about them?"

Walker took out his notebook.

115

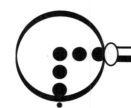

"We've spent the last two days," he said, "checking the activities of the gang members that night. So far, we've learned only enough to be sure of the following:

"1. If Chase is guilty and Heath is innocent, then Decker is guilty.
"2. If Chase is innocent, then Mullaney is innocent.
"3. If Heath is guilty, then Mullaney is guilty.
"4. Chase and Heath are not both guilty.
"5. Unless Heath is guilty, Decker is innocent.

"That's all of it, Tom. Not many hard facts, I'm afraid. The heat is really on, though, so if you can deduce anything more from what we have, I'll be very grateful."

Stanwick accepted the notebook and studied its scribbled entries with complete absorption. Walker, still agitated and restless, got up and paced the floor.

A few moments later, Stanwick closed the notebook and looked up with a smile.

"Well, Matt," he said cheerfully, "it's about time you relaxed. You've given me enough to determine who is guilty and who is innocent in this matter."

Who assaulted the deputy mayor?

Solution on page 158

INSPECTOR WALKER

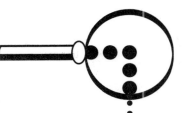

STANWICK VISITS SCOTLAND YARD

"Stanwick, my dear fellow," exclaimed Bodwin, "you couldn't possibly have chosen a better moment to come to London."

"London in April hasn't quite the reputation of the French capital," replied Thomas P. Stanwick with a grin as he sat down. "Still, I'm always glad to be back."

The amateur logician had stopped at Scotland Yard to visit his old friend Inspector Gilbert Bodwin. Stanwick was in London for a week to attend a Churchill Society dinner in Pall Mall.

"I expect this must be a particularly busy time for you," Stanwick continued, "with the foreign ministers' conference only a week away."

Bodwin leaned forward intently across his desk. "It is indeed, and that's why I'm glad to have a chance to talk with you."

"Oh?" Stanwick finished lighting his pipe and peered at Bodwin curiously through a cloud of smoke.

"Yes, and the Prime Minister is furious at the breach in security. Some important state papers were taken from a safe

at the Foreign and Commonwealth Office two nights ago, at about nine-thirty. From the way it was done, we know the thief had to have known the combination of the safe.

"We have three suspects. They are all clerks in the FCO: James Malcolm, Samuel Hickory, and William Dell. Each knows the combination as part of his duties."

Stanwick, full of interest, absentmindedly fingered a tip of his mustache.

"Of course you've questioned them," he said. "Just what accounts do they give of their whereabouts on the evening of the theft?"

Bodwin flipped open a notebook. "Malcolm says he went to the theatre with his wife that evening. "

The inspector produced four scraps of paper, which Stanwick recognized as the halves of two torn tickets.

"He showed us these from his jacket pocket," Bodwin went on. "As you can see, they are for that evening's 8:00 o'clock performance of 'Coningsby' at the Disraeli Playhouse in Southwark. The play lasted until ten, and the ushers say no one left early. The Malcolms live in Chiswick and say they travelled to and from the theatre in their own car.

"Hickory maintains that he was engrossed in a darts tournament at his neighborhood pub from eight until eleven that night. That's the Sacred Cow in St. John's Wood. I have statements here from several of the regulars, all of whom confirm that Hickory was there the whole time."

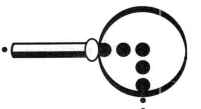

"Does he often play darts there?" asked Stanwick.

"The regulars say he stops by about twice a week for an evening pint," Bodwin replied, "but he hardly ever plays darts."

"How about Dell?"

"He's the only one without an alibi that we could readily verify. He lives alone and says he spent the whole evening watching television. He told my sergeant the plots of all that evening's BBC1 programs, but he's still our prime suspect. There just isn't anything solid to go on."

"Does he also live in town?"

Bodwin nodded. "Small flat in Belgrave Road. Any suggestions? The P. M. will want my head on a platter if we don't nab our man."

Stanwick laughed and languidly stood up.

"I'm ready for a bite of lunch," he said. "If you'll join me in a stroll to the little pub I saw down the street, I'll be glad to tell you the identity of the thief."

Who stole the documents?

Solution on page 158

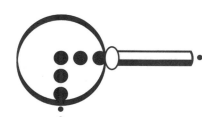

THE EXPLORER'S TALE

Thomas P. Stanwick, the amateur logician, had seldom been so surprised or delighted. In return for what he considered a few trifling deductions that had helped avert the disruption of an important state conference in London, the Queen had given him free passage back to the United States aboard a luxury passenger liner.

Stanwick quickly fell into the routine on board and began to enjoy the cruise thoroughly. By day he strode the deck, read, played games, or leaned against the railing and gazed out at the dark waters of the North Atlantic. By night he dined in elegance with the other passengers and then relaxed in one of the ship's lounges, engrossed in conversation, chess, cards, or a good book.

On the evening of the sixth day, Stanwick was sitting in a comfortable armchair and listening to a long travelogue by Gregory Justin, a self-proclaimed adventurer and explorer. Justin, a stout, middle-aged man with a ruddy face and thinning red hair, leaned toward Stanwick and spoke with obvious relish.

"Later that year," he went on, "I led an expedition of 20 on a photographic tour of the jungles and plains of Zambia. We were there almost three months, and what a time we had! The jungles were dark and beautiful but safe enough, as long as we were careful about the occasional snake or tiger that crossed our path. On the plain, though, we once had a pretty harrowing night.

"We had spent that day photographing an elephant herd and a pride of lions. The male lions slept most of the day, but when they shook their great manes and looked up, they were a magnificent sight.

"We made camp that night on the plain, about two miles from the pride. At two-thirty, I was awakened by some yelling. A rogue lioness with a dangerous appetite had found our camp and was clawing at some of the tents. I looked out and could see her in the moonlight, so I grabbed my rifle, got her in my sights, and put her down. I hated to do it, but it was necessary."

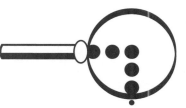

"You had quite an exciting time, I guess," remarked Stanwick with a smile. He arose lazily and shook hands with Justin. "Thank you. I enjoyed your stories. I have some letters to write this evening, so I'll now wish you a good night."

Before returning to his cabin, Stanwick stepped out on deck and strolled to the railing. A few sparks from his pipe danced out into the inky void.

"Justin's a fine storyteller," he muttered to himself. "It's a pity his stories aren't entirely true!"

What flaw did Stanwick find in Justin's story?

Solution on page 158

THE CASE OF THE REINDEER SPIES

The ringing of the doorbell cut through the clacking of the keyboard in Thomas P. Stanwick's small study. The amateur logician arose from the history textbook he was editing and went to the door. Rufus, his black labrador, lifted his head sleepily from his paws.

"Mr. Stanwick?" A tall man in a brown suit flashed a badge. "I'm Special Agent Stevens of the F.B.I. Inspector Walker of the Royston Police referred me to you. Do you mind if I come in?"

"Not at all." Though surprised by the visit, Stanwick showed Stevens into the living room with quiet geniality. It was not the first time that he had received unusual visitors through Walker's recommendations.

Stevens glanced curiously around at the crowded bookshelves, the wall maps, and the papers and dusty chess sets piled on various side tables. Declining Stanwick's offer of tea, he seated himself in an armchair near the hearth. Stanwick sat down in an armchair across from him and relit his pipe.

"Matt Walker is a good friend of mine, Mr. Stevens," he said, "and I'm always glad to help him or an associate of his if I can. I presume that in this case I may be of some service to the government."

"Exactly, Mr. Stanwick," replied Stevens. "I've come to you because this case has a tangled knot of facts, and Walker says you can untangle such knots better than anyone else he knows. We are also aware, of course, of your past services to the American and British governments.

"Briefly, the facts are these. As a result of the national effort to crack down on domestic spies, the Bureau has uncovered a ring of five spies in Royston who have started selling defense industry secrets to the Chinese consulate in New York. The five individuals have been identified, and we are intercepting their messages.

"We believe they may be able to lead us to several similar rings in the Midwest, so we want to continue monitoring their messages a while longer before we arrest them. Our problem is that they refer to each other in code names, and we need to match the individuals to the code names before we can completely understand the messages."

Stanwick reached lazily for a pad of paper and a pencil. "What do you have so far?" he asked.

Stevens opened a notebook.

"The code names," he said with a slight smile, "are those of well-known reindeer: Comet, Cupid, Dasher, Dancer, and Donder. We are certain that these names correspond in some order to the members of the group, all of whom live in Royston.

"Sal Abelardo is a civil engineer for Spacetech. His wife works for a publishing company and apparently knows nothing of his espionage activities. Peter Bircham works as a janitor for the same firm. He is single. John Cantrell is a junior executive with Aeroco. He and his wife share a condo downtown with his sister. Tim Delmarin, unmarried, is a communications expert with the same firm. The fifth member is Telly Ephesos, a retired Foreign Service Officer who spent twenty years in China. He is married and has no siblings."

Stanwick puffed on his pipe and wrote quietly on the pad, while Rufus delicately sniffed the visitor's briefcase.

"From the messages already sent," continued Stevens, "and our own investigation, we've been able to glean only a few facts. Cantrell and 'Dasher' and their wives sometimes take vacations together. 'Cupid' is highly dissatisfied with his job. Mrs. Abelardo regularly corresponds with 'Mrs. Donder.' Neither 'Comet' nor 'Dasher' has ever been outside the state. Mrs. Abelardo was once engaged to the brother of 'Donder.' Finally, Bircham makes monthly trips to Mexico City.

"I cannot impress upon you enough, Mr. Stanwick, the importance of identifying these code names. Any help you could give us in this matter would be greatly appreciated."

Stanwick, too preoccupied to answer immediately, paused and fingered a tip of his mustache as languid wisps of smoke curled up from his pipe. A moment later he scribbled something on his pad and tossed it to Stevens.

"Here are the code names and their possessors. Happy hunting!"

Who has which code name?

Solution on page 158

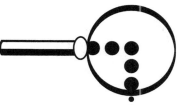

STANWICK AND THE ACCIDENTAL THIEF

Thomas P. Stanwick roamed the Christmas-lit aisles of Schweppe's Department Store, looking for the right gift for his old friend Annie Tynsdale. Annie owned a candy shop in Cambridge, England.

The women's accessories aisle seemed safe enough. He strolled down it slowly, eying successive displays of purses, handkerchiefs, wallets, coin purses, scarves, and gloves. Though the prices on the tags were unexpectedly high, the goods were all handsome and of good quality. He paused by the glove table and picked up a pair.

Just then a small commotion at the front of the store attracted his attention. Jim Sperlich, the store detective, had just re-entered the store grasping a young blond woman firmly by the arm. In his other hand he held a brown leather coin purse. The woman, her face flushed, struggled to free her arm.

"Let me go, you gorilla," she spat. "I was going to pay for it!"

"We'll let the store manager decide," Sperlich replied stolidly. "Just come along, please." He guided her toward a small office in the back of the store.

Stanwick, who knew both Sperlich and the store manager, Dale Carpenter, decided to be on hand. Putting down the gloves, he strode to Carpenter's office, which was closer to him than to Sperlich and his captive.

"Merry Christmas, Dale!" he exclaimed to Carpenter, who looked up from his papers with a start. "How's business these days?"

"Hello, Tom! Why, it's not too —"

"Excuse me, Mr. Carpenter." Sperlich arrived with the woman, and Stanwick smiled and smoothly stepped to a corner of the office. "Hi, Tom. I caught this lady shoplifting, Mr. Carpenter. I spotted her just as she was thrusting this coin purse into her jacket pocket, and stayed near her until she left the premises without paying for it. Then I apprehended her."

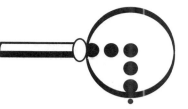

"It's all an innocent mistake!" exclaimed the woman, wrenching her arm free at last and facing Carpenter angrily. "I intended to pay for it. I'm just absent-minded, and forgot at the last minute that I had it."

Carpenter took the coin purse and quickly examined its leather exterior. Snapping it open, he checked the lining and extracted the price tag.

"One of our better brands of ladies' coin purses," he noted. "May I ask, Ms. —"

"Leonard. Celia Leonard."

"May I ask, Ms. Leonard, why you put this purse in your pocket?"

"I tucked it away—temporarily—because I wanted to try on a few pairs of gloves, and so needed to free my hands." She turned angrily to Sperlich. "Isn't that right, Mr. Hot Shot Detective? If you were staying so close to me, you must have seen me try on the gloves."

Sperlich's face flushed a little.

"Well, it's true, Mr. Carpenter," he replied. "After putting the purse in her pocket, she did try on three or four pairs of gloves. And put them all back."

"See there?" She smiled at the manager in cold triumph. "Now please let me pay for or return the coin purse and be on my way."

Carpenter scratched his balding head. "Well, I don't know. Technically, of course, you are guilty of shoplifting by leaving the store without paying for the item, whether or not you intended to do so. However, since there seems to be good reason to believe that it wasn't intentional, maybe —"

"Just a moment, Dale." Stanwick interrupted him and stepped forward. "This lady's theft of the coin purse was quite intentional, and I think you should press charges."

How does Stanwick know that she intended to steal the purse?

Solution on page 158

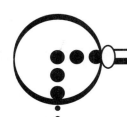

THE McPHERSON-McTAVISH MYSTERY

Early one drizzly morning, as Thomas P. Stanwick was finishing breakfast at the White Lion Inn, the innkeeper told him he was wanted on the phone. This surprised him, since he was on the third day of a vacation in Dartmoor, England, and few people knew he was there.

"Mr. Stanwick? This is Inspector Carstairs," said the voice on the phone.

"Oh, yes." The amateur logician had met the inspector at the local pub two days earlier and had swapped crime stories with him. "What can I do for you?"

"Colonel Rogers was murdered in his library last evening. Since you've been helpful in other police investigations, I thought you might be interested in dropping by and having a look at this one."

"Thank you, Carstairs, I'd be delighted."

The Rogers estate was only two miles across the moor from the inn, so within an hour Stanwick had walked to the main house, scraped the sticky red clay of the moor from his feet, and joined Carstairs in the library. Colonel Rogers lay in front of his desk, shot in the chest at point-blank range.

Carstairs pointed to two grizzled, middle-aged men sitting sullenly nearby.

"That's McTavish on the right and McPherson on the left. McTavish is a neighbor and McPherson is the groundskeeper here. McTavish says he saw McPherson bury the murder weapon, a shotgun, in the garden last evening."

"That's right, sir," cried McTavish. "I had my telescope set up just a few miles away on a little knoll on the moor. Before lookin' out at the stars, I swung it around the landscape a bit—to test it, you know. That's when I saw him come out, look around, and bury the gun."

"A rotten lie!" roared McPherson. "I was in my cottage all evening until the constable came knocking last night."

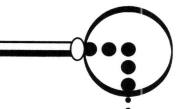

"That's enough!" Carstairs warned. "We dug up that shotgun last night from the spot in the garden that McTavish showed us. All indications are that it's the murder weapon."

Stanwick examined the dirty shotgun leaning against the wall. Beside the shotgun was a golf bag with a broken strap, scuffed along the bottom but otherwise unmarked. Inside, however, Stanwick found no clubs, but telescopic equipment instead.

"Is this your golf bag, Mr. McTavish?" he asked.

"Aye. Every week for months now, I've dragged that bag with my telescope from the village up to the knoll to look at the stars."

"Wasn't it too cloudy last night for that?"

"No, it rained a bit in the afternoon, but by dusk it had cleared some."

"How could you see Mr. McPherson at night?"

"Oh, at dusk it was still light enough to see what he was doin'."

Stanwick sat down in a nearby armchair and fingered the tip of his mustache.

"Mr. McPherson," he asked, "did you hear a shot last night?"

"No, sir," was the reply. "My cottage is some distance from the library."

"Who called you, Carstairs?"

"I received a call from McTavish, who said he had just rushed back to the village. We picked him up with his equipment, came here, discovered the body, and found the gun where he said McPherson had buried it."

"Any fingerprints?"

129

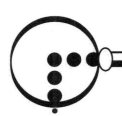

"None left on the gun, and only those of the colonel in the room. Also, the housekeeper tells me an ivory-handled knife is missing from his desk."

"Well, well." Stanwick abruptly arose and faced McTavish. "I think you had better start telling the truth, Mr. McTavish. Your story is a lie!"

How does Stanwick know McTavish is lying?

Solution on page 159

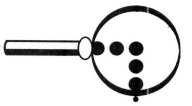

MURDER IN A LONDON FLAT

Lord Calinore was gunned down in his London flat by a robber, who then ransacked the flat. The case was placed in the capable hands of Inspector Gilbert Bodwin of Scotland Yard. Bodwin's investigation revealed that one man had planned the crime, another had carried it out, and a third had acted as lookout.

Bodwin discussed the case at length one evening over dinner at his club with an old friend, Thomas P. Stanwick, the amateur logician, visiting from America.

"It's quite a case," Stanwick remarked. "Have you any suspects?"

Bodwin sliced his roast beef with relish. "Yes, indeed. Four. We have conclusive evidence that three of those four were responsible for the crime."

"Really! That's remarkable progress. What about the fourth?"

"He had no prior knowledge of the crime and is completely innocent. The problem is that we're not sure which of the four are the planner, the gunman, the lookout, and the innocent bystander."

"I see." Stanwick took more Yorkshire pudding. "What do you know about them at this point?"

"Well, the names of the four are Merrick, Cross, Llewellyn, and Halifax. Halifax and Cross play golf together every Saturday. They're an odd pair! Halifax can't drive, and Cross has been out of Dartmoor Prison for only a year."

"What was he in for?"

"Forgery. We know that Merrick and Halifax kept the flat under surveillance for several days just before the day the crime was committed, the 17th. Llewellyn and Merrick, with their wives, had dinner together on the Strand on the 12th."

"An interesting compilation," said Stanwick, "but hardly conclusive. Is that all of it?"

"Not quite. We know that the gunman spent the week before the crime in Edinburgh, and that the innocent bystander was acquainted with the planner and the gunman, but not with the lookout."

"That is very helpful," said Stanwick with a smile. He raised his wine glass. "Bodwin, old fellow, your case is complete."

Who are the planner, the gunman, and the lookout?

Solution on page 159

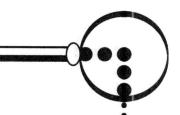

THE ROAD TO TRIGOON

It was August in the Scottish Highlands, and Thomas P. Stanwick, the amateur logician, strode happily along the road. He was well along on a hundred-mile walking holiday, and the exercise had invigorated his lanky but usually sedentary frame. Three days more would see him to Cape Wrath and the end of his journey.

Stanwick was passing through an isolated and little-known area of the Highlands inhabited exclusively by members of two clans, the MacDurgalls and the MacFurbishes. They had lived there for many centuries, and abided by time-honored customs. The oldest of these was

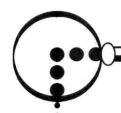

that the MacDurgalls always told the truth and the MacFurbishes always lied. The origin of this peculiar tradition was long forgotten, but the tradition itself was rigorously observed.

Stanwick intended to stay the night in Trigoon, a village in a distant glen. His map of the region, however, was sketchy. As he rounded a bend, admiring the verdant hills around him, he came upon an unexpected fork in the road.

No direction sign was to be seen. Fortunately, three inhabitants of the region were sitting by the wayside, eating their lunches after working in a nearby field. Stanwick approached them.

"Excuse me," he said, "but which of these is the road to Trigoon?"

"The road on the right," replied the first man.

"The road on the left," said the second man.

"Either road is fine," said the third man.

The first man jumped up angrily and faced the second man. "You're lying!" he roared.

"No, you are!" said the second man, coming to his feet.

The third man also came to his feet. "Bruce speaks the truth!" he said angrily to the first man.

The three of them continued arguing fiercely among themselves. Stanwick smiled, murmured his thanks, and set off along the road to Trigoon.

Which is the road to Trigoon?

Solution on page 159

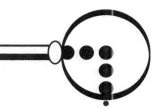

THE MATTER OF
THE McALISTER MURDERS

Whit Knowlton, a retired lawyer in his eighties, loved to reminisce about his trials. His memory was shaky, however, and he sometimes had to let his listeners fill in blank spots in his narrative.

One lazy Sunday afternoon in the summer, Knowlton was sitting in his well-stocked library swapping stories with Thomas P. Stanwick. The amateur logician always enjoyed his visits with Knowlton.

"The McAlister murders in Baltimore hit the papers in the winter of 1953," said the lawyer. "Four men were arrested for the murders within a week, and I was called in to assist the district attorney.

"All four were indicted, but evidence brought out in the course of the trial proved that only two of them were guilty. Our problem was to find out which two they were."

"How useful was their testimony?" asked Stanwick.

"Oh, useful enough, as it turned out," Knowlton replied. "The first defendant, Addler, said that either the second defendant, Byran, was guilty, or the fourth defendant, Derrick, was innocent. Byran said that he was innocent, and that either Addler or Collins, the third defendant, was guilty.

"Collins said that Byran and Derrick were not both guilty. Derrick, after a long refusal to speak at all, said that Collins was innocent if and only if Addler was also innocent."

"Were any of their statements proven true?" Stanwick asked.

"Well, yes. Other evidence proved that the two guilty ones were lying and the two innocent ones were telling the truth. Unfortunately, I don't quite remember anymore who the guilty ones were."

Stanwick smiled and fumbled in his pocket for his pipe.

"This case is a treat, Whit," he said, "for it's not too hard to deduce who the guilty ones were."

Who were the guilty ones?

Solution on page 159

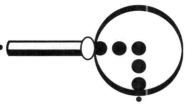

DEATH IN THE GARAGE

Inspector Matthew Walker and Thomas P. Stanwick had barely begun their weekly game that Thursday evening at the chess club when Walker's beeper went off.

"There's been a suspicious death in Caterina Road," said Walker when he returned from the phone. "Probably a suicide. Care to come?"

"By all means. Some evenings weren't made for chess."

A quarter of an hour later, Walker and Stanwick were in the garage of Walter McCarthy, a real estate broker. McCarthy was seated behind the wheel of his car, dead. The garage door was open, the car was silent, and the police were busily at work.

"The body was discovered by Mrs. McCarthy when she returned home on foot about six," reported Sergeant Hatch. "The car was running. Nearly overcome by exhaust fumes herself, she opened the garage door from the inside, switched off the car, and called 9-1-1 from the kitchen. She's inside now."

"Cause of death established?" asked Walker.

"The medical examiner says the body shows every sign of carbon monoxide asphyxiation. We did find these in the right jacket pocket, though." Hatch handed Walker a plastic evidence bag containing a pill bottle. Walker gingerly removed the bottle, glanced at the label, and popped open the cap. The bottle was half full of large, pink lozenges.

"A prescription depressant," he remarked. "Refilled only yesterday for one pill a day, and yet half the pills are gone. Could these have killed him?"

"No, they couldn't," responded Dr. Pillsbury, the owlish medical examiner, who now approached Walker. "If he took half the bottle, though, the dose would have knocked him out in about fifteen seconds."

"But why would he take the pills if he were about to asphyxiate himself anyway?" asked Stanwick. "Asphyxiation is painless."

Pillsbury shrugged. "It is. But he may have wanted to put himself under sooner, before he could lose his nerve. I've seen it before in suicides."

"Hatch," said Walker, turning to the sergeant, "what was found in the car?"

"Nothing unusual, sir. Registration, maps, ice scraper, a scarf, a bag of chips. A folder of house listings. In the trunk, some tools, a spare, jumper cables, a blanket."

"Has a suicide note turned up?"

"Not yet, sir. We're still checking the house."

"And how much gas was in the tank?" asked Stanwick.

"Oh, plenty, sir. More than enough."

"Thank you, sergeant," said Walker. "Please tell Mrs. McCarthy I'll see her soon."

"Yes, sir."

As Hatch strode off, Walker turned back to Stanwick.

"Well, Tom, I'm afraid there's not much of special interest here. Whether or not we find a note, this looks to me like a straightforward suicide."

Stanwick shook his head solemnly.

"I don't think so, Matt," he replied. "Though I can't be certain, I think this is a case of murder."

Why does Stanwick think McCarthy was murdered?

Solution on page 160

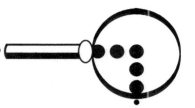

MURDER AT THE CHESSBOARD

Thomas P. Stanwick and Inspector Matthew Walker were seated one afternoon in Stanwick's living room, chatting about recent crime news.

"You may have seen something in the papers," said Walker, "about the murder two nights ago of Professor Richard Hansford."

"Yes, I think so." Stanwick frowned. "The archaeologist. He was stabbed in the back while seated at a chessboard in his study, wasn't he? Killed instantly."

"That's right. A call came in to headquarters at 8:30 last Wednesday night from Michael Rimbach, a visiting relative of Hansford's.

"When the squad car arrived, Rimbach explained to the officers that he had heard a cry from the study as he was passing by in the hallway. Looking in, he saw the professor slumped back in his chair and caught a glimpse of a man escaping through the French doors of the study onto the lawn. Rimbach rushed to the doors, but the man had already disappeared into the rainy darkness.

"Hansford was obviously dead, so without touching anything, Rimbach called the police and told Hansford's sister Emily of the crime. Emily, an invalid, had heard nothing.

"Rimbach thinks he recognized the man as David Kunst, a neighbor who played chess with Hansford every Wednesday evening at 7:30. They were both enthusiasts of monochromatic chess, and played no other kind."

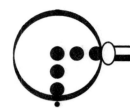

"Really?" said Stanwick. "Chess in which no piece can move from a black square to a white square, or vice versa? That's quite rare."

"Yes, it is, which is why they played it so regularly. It's hard to find partners for it. Rimbach, the sister, and Kunst all confirmed the weekly games.

"When we interviewed Kunst at his home later that evening," Walker continued, "he said he had received a call from Rimbach a little after seven saying that Hansford was ill and had to cancel that evening's game. Kunst said he therefore spent the evening at home. Rimbach denies having called him. Kunst lives alone, and there were no witnesses. We saw a damp overcoat and shoes there, but he says they got wet on his way home from work."

"In what condition did you find the study?" Stanwick asked.

"The French doors were open. We looked for footprint traces on the lawn, but found nothing definite. The condition of the board indicated that a game was in progress when the murder occurred."

"Did the board look like the game had been in progress for an hour?"

"Yes, I guess so. It looked like the players were entering the middle part of the game. A knight and two bishops were already posted in the center of the board."

"Had the weekly game ever been called off before?"

"Now and then. Usually the sister phoned Kunst if Hansford was ill. She had been confined to her bed that day, though, and hadn't seen her brother."

"Well," said Stanwick, fingering the tip of his mustache, "you have an interesting but thoroughly contradictory pair of stories to consider. One of them is patently untrue, however, so I suggest you concentrate your inquiry in the direction of the liar."

Who is lying?

Solution on page 160

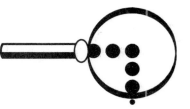

THE NORFOLK BANK ROBBERY

Thomas P. Stanwick, the amateur logician, was a familiar and welcome visitor at Royston Police headquarters. Shortly after noon on a fine Tuesday in spring, he returned a nod to the duty sergeant and strolled to the office of Inspector Matt Walker.

"The Ides of April are almost upon us, my lad," said Stanwick cheerily. Walker looked up from the piles of papers on his desk with a weary smile.

"Tax time! Don't remind me," he said. "It's good to see you though, Tom."

"What's been happening?" Stanwick began to fill his pipe.

"How about a bank robbery?"

"A bank robbery!" Stanwick laughed. "Isn't that a bit old-fashioned, what with electronic transfers and all? I suppose you'll be investigating a stagecoach holdup next."

"You'd be surprised, Tom," Walker replied. "Banks still handle quite a lot of actual cash, and that still attracts the bad guys."

"Indeed!," said Stanwick, arching his eyebrows. "What bank got held up?"

"Last Friday, about two o'clock," related Walker, "two men wearing Halloween masks entered the Norfolk Bank and Trust and demanded the money in the teller cages and in the safe. One man kept a gun drawn while the other collected the cash in a burlap sack. During some last-minute confusion, the gunman shot a teller. Luckily, she'll be all right. The two made off with about $77,000 and were driven from the scene by a third man in a blue Toyota."

Stanwick grunted. "What have you found out since then?"

"A good deal." Walker leaned forward intently. "We got a partial license number off the car, and have been canvassing our street informants. We're now convinced that the three belong to a small syndicate composed of five men: Howard Kuhlman, Thomas Brinner, Will Lan-

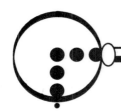

gley, George Pickett, and Fred Schartner. We don't know much about them, but so far have been able to assemble the following facts:

"1. Kuhlman and the shooter were seen together at Arnie's Pool Hall on Friday night. Kuhlman won two out of three games.

"2. Langley never participated in a crime without Brinner, whom he admired like a kid brother. Both used to work at a local electronics plant.

"3. Pickett was involved in the robbery. Despite his phobia about guns, which he refuses to touch, he once worked as a private security guard.

"4. Schartner and Langley were both involved in the robbery or the driver was either Kuhlman or Schartner.

"5. The driver is a champion bowler. He doesn't know any other games, but he lifts weights to stay in shape.

"Naturally, our main concern is identifying the shooter," concluded Walker, "but we're eager to identify all three involved in the robbery and their roles."

"Well, Matt," said Stanwick with a smile, "if you're sure of your facts, I can identify each of the three robbers right now."

Who were the shooter, the driver, and the collector?

Solution on page 160

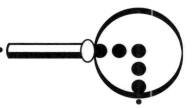

THE SCOTTISH SERVANTS

The summer afternoon was fading when Thomas P. Stanwick returned from a hike in the Highland hills and entered the imposing Scottish mansion of the Earl of Stanwyck. The earl was sitting at an oak table in his book-lined study, working on some papers. Stanwick, who was visiting his distant cousin, strolled in and flopped into a large armchair in front of the table.

"What a fine day!" he exclaimed. "You really should go out and get some exercise, James."

"I'd like nothing better," the earl replied. "Unfortunately, Her Majesty's government requires that these census forms be completed and mailed by tomorrow."

"Census forms?" Stanwick laughed. "That chore shouldn't take you long."

"It's not quite that simple, Thomas." The earl put down his pencil and leaned back in his chair. "The wretched form asks the ages of the principal members of my household staff: Jermyn, the butler; Harding, the chief gardener; Mrs. Morgan, the housekeeper; and the maids, Nellie and Mollie. And I don't know what their ages are."

"Why don't you ask them?"

"Because it just wouldn't be proper." The earl snatched up his pencil in irritation. "The staff here are all good Scots and reticent about their private lives. If I were to ask a personal question, I'm sure they would resent the invasion of their privacy. It sounds silly, I know, but the matter does require some delicate handling."

"I see." Stanwick suppressed a grin and fumbled in his pockets for his pipe and tobacco. "Do you have any information to go on?"

"Just a few scraps."

"Good! What are they?"

"Let's see now." The earl frowned in concentration. "I did once hear the housekeeper chastise Mollie for something and say that she had '20 more years of living' than Mollie had."

144

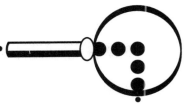

"That's helpful," said Stanwick. "For my part, I remember learning on my visit three years ago that the chief gardener was 12 years younger than the butler."

"Indeed! I recall that it was about that time that Mrs. Morgan mentioned something about being three years older than Harding."

"I have a confession to make, cousin," Stanwick said with a smile. "Nellie and Mollie are obviously close to each other in age. A few days ago, being curious about this and not knowing as much about Scottish reticence as I do now, I asked them how old they were. Mollie only smiled, but Nellie said that when Mrs. Morgan was the age Mollie is now, she was four times as old as Nellie was then. 'Figure that out, Mr. Logic Man!' she said with a laugh. Of course, I couldn't figure out a thing."

"So much for simply asking the staff!" laughed the earl. "I have only one item to add. Jermyn and Harding sometimes drink together when off duty, and they concoct the strangest reasons for toasts and celebrations. Just a couple of weeks ago, I came across them in one of the village pubs. They said they were celebrating the fact that the average of their ages had passed the half-century mark, and was in fact 51."

"Excellent!" exclaimed Stanwick. "That information will, I think, allow the staff to retain their reticence, such as it is, and you to complete your paperwork. "

How old are the earl's staff?

Solution on page 160

THE CASE OF THE PURLOINED PRESENTS

Christmas in Baskerville! Two feet of snow covered the ground, and colored lights and wreaths festooned the houses. On Wright Avenue, the Baskerville Charity Center invited all comers to partake of hot soup, fresh rolls, and coffee, gratis.

When Thomas P. Stanwick, the amateur logician, arrived at the center the day before Christmas as a volunteer to serve soup and coffee, however, the center manager, Betty Davidson, rushed up to him.

"Oh, Tom, it's terrible!" she told him in an angrily quivering voice.

"What's wrong, Betty?"

"Why, someone's taken the sack of presents! You know, the big sack of Christmas toys we collect for the children every year. Thirty pounds of toys. It was in the corner by the door, and I saw it there two hours ago, but now it's gone!"

"All right now, calm down." Stanwick laid a soothing hand on Davidson's shoulder. "Let's figure out what happened. Are you sure the sack was there then?"

"I'm positive!"

"And neither you nor any of the staff has moved it since?"

"No, I've checked. None of us has touched it."

Stanwick glanced around the room. About two dozen customers, most of them men, were sitting at the long tables, eating or playing cards or board games. Several backpacks and other bundles lay along the walls of the room or beside their owners. Stanwick and Davidson sat down at an unoccupied end of one of the tables to talk.

"Most of your customers are regulars," Stanwick noted, "and you probably know everyone here. Is there anyone who was here two hours ago but who isn't here now?"

Davidson thought for a moment. "Only three," she said. "Jim Brennan, Ollie Hunter, and Jerry McNutt left during that time. I've also looked over the bags, knapsacks and bundles here, and can account for them. Their owners are still here."

147

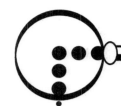

"Jim Brennan," mumured Stanwick. "He has a bad back, doesn't he?"

"Yes. A job injury. He could carry his ten-pound knapsack, but not much else."

"Do you particularly remember seeing any of the three coming or going?"

"I saw Hunter come in with an ordinary backpack. Didn't see him leave, though. McNutt came in with a pack on his back and carrying two suitcases. I didn't see him leave either. Didn't see Brennan coming or going, but saw him while he was here."

"Hmmm." Stanwick lit his pipe and smoked thoughtfully for a few minutes. "Look here, Betty," he said at last, "if I got the presents back for you, would you agree not to press charges?"

Davidson's face flushed in astonishment. "What do you mean, Tom?"

Stanwick smiled.

"You see, I think I know who the thief is," he said, "and I happen to know that he's had some hard luck this year. Never stole before, and probably did on impulse this time. The sack should still be intact, and I'm sure that I can persuade him to return it. I might even chip in for his kids on my own behalf."

Davidson's face softened. "And I thought you were so relentless, Tom."

"Well, it's Christmas. And he's really not a bad fellow."

"All right, go ahead. I won't prosecute. But at least tell me who it is!"

Who is the thief?

Solution on page 161

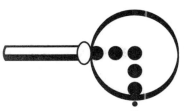

THE CASE OF
THE THREE CONFESSORS

Thomas P. Stanwick was holding court in the Royston Chess Club lounge one evening, reminiscing to friends about the previous summer.

"You've heard me speak of Knordwyn, the curious village in Northumbria," he said. "About half of the villagers always speak the truth, and the other half always lie. While I was staying a week or so at the Grey Boar Inn near the village, a valuable golden mace was stolen from the historical society's tiny museum."

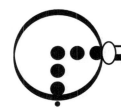

"The mace was discovered two days later, hidden in a leather shop in the village. The thief had apparently stored it there temporarily. The only ones who could have done this were three workmen in the shop named Appleby, Barrows, and Connor. They were therefore arrested as suspects.

"A preliminary hearing was held before the bewigged local magistrate," Stanwick continued. "It seemed that most of the village crowded into the little courtroom the day the three suspects were questioned. I arrived early and got a good seat behind the prosecutor's table.

"The local authorites wanted to know, of course, who had stolen the mace. They also wanted to know just when it had been stolen. Each suspect was questioned on both points and, much to the astonishment of the court, each offered up a confession. The statements were as follows:

Appleby: 1. I stole the mace. 2. I either committed the theft alone or had Connor as an accomplice. 3. The mace was stolen either late Wednesday afternoon or Wednesday night.

Barrows: 1. I stole the mace. 2. Appleby was my accomplice. 3. The mace was stolen late Wednesday afternoon.

Connors: 1. I stole the mace. 2. Neither Appleby nor Barrows was involved in the theft. 3. The mace was stolen late Wednesday afternoon.

"Well! The prosecutor plainly didn't know what to make of this. Court procedure mandated that a decision would have to be based on the statements of the suspects and the knowledge that each was a villager and therefore either a consistent liar or a consistent truth-teller.

"At this point, I jotted down a note and passed it to the prosecutor. As he read it, a measure of calm returned to his troubled countenance. He then stood to address the magistrate.

"'M'lud,' he said, 'I am pleased to say that it is now possible to identify who stole the article in question, and when the crime was committed.' Which, with the help of my note, he proceeded to do. Can any of you?"

Who stole the mace, and when was it stolen?

Solution on page 161

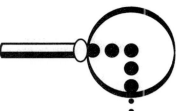

BLACKMAIL AT CITY HALL

The Honorable Christopher Hawkins, one of the two deputy mayors of the city of Royston, was pacing his office in uncharacteristic agitation when Inspector Matthew Walker of the police department and Thomas P. Stanwick, the amateur logician, arrived.

"There's the note, Inspector," said Hawkins, pointing to a creased piece of paper on his desk blotter. "As crude an attempt at blackmail as you've ever seen, I'll bet."

Walker and Stanwick went to the desk and read the note, which was composed with pasted words and letters cut out of a newspaper:

HAWKINS YOU BIGAMIST
PREPARE TO PAY 20K OR BE RUINED
MORE LATER

"Why would anyone call you a bigamist?" asked Walker.

Hawkins shook his head angrily.

"Some years ago," he said, "questions were raised about the legality of my divorce from my first wife, but they have long since been put to rest. I'm not eager to have them raised again just now, but of course I won't pay anything to stop it."

"I see," said Walker. "This note arrived this morning?"

"Yes. The envelope is beside it."

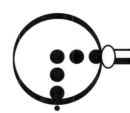

Walker looked closely at the small brown envelope. It had canceled postage, no return address, and was typed:

DEPUTY MAYOR
CITY HALL
ROYSTON

"A typed envelope, in order not to attract particular attention during delivery," remarked Stanwick. "But the blackmailer didn't want to use the typewriter any more than necessary, for fear that it might later be identified. Hence the use of newspaper clippings for the note itself, and the extreme conciseness of the address, which omits the state and ZIP code."

"Quite so," replied Walker. "The cancellation indicates that it was mailed downtown, probably at a corner box. There was enough of an address, of course, to get it here."

Stanwick turned to Hawkins. "Who delivers the outside mail to your office?"

"We have several mail clerks. The senior clerk, Hank Blair, sorts the mail in the mail room. Other clerks then deliver it to the various offices."

"Had the envelope been opened and resealed when you received it?"

"Why, no. My secretary is out sick today, so I opened my mail myself. I'm sure the envelope still had its original seal."

Walker glanced over the note again. "The fingerprint team will be here shortly," he said, "but I doubt that the blackmailer was so careless as to leave prints."

"Even before then, Matt," said Stanwick, "I think you should question this clerk, Blair, and check his typewriter. He knows something about this matter!

Why does Stanwick suspect Blair's involvement?

Solution on page 161

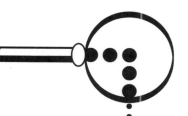

THE CHURCHILL LETTER

"Mrs. Bryant! It's nice to see you again. Please come in." Thomas P. Stanwick stood back from the door and waved his gray-haired visitor into his living room.

"I'm sorry to bother you again, Mr. Stanwick," said Ellen Bryant as she settled herself onto the sofa, "but you were so helpful with my earlier difficulty that I hoped you might advise me on this one."

"Certainly, if I can," replied Stanwick. Striding to the sideboard, he began to prepare a tray of fresh tea. "What's the problem?"

"A few days ago," she said, "I was visited by Stephen Faybush, the nephew of a couple I know in my neighborhood. He specializes in unusual investments."

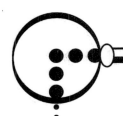

"Indeed?" said Stanwick. He brought the tray over and poured two cups of Lapsang souchong. "Have you been looking for investment advice?"

"Well, I have a small nest egg that isn't earning much in the bank, and I may have mentioned this to my neighbors."

"And what sort of investments does this Faybush promote?"

"Historical artifacts, mostly. Famous signatures and such. He says they consistently beat inflation as they rise in value over time."

"That's true—if they are genuine, that is." Stanwick settled himself near her on the sofa. "Do you by chance have such an item in your folder there?"

"Exactly, yes." Mrs Bryant opened a manila folder she had been carrying and extracted a letter. "It's a Churchill," she said as she handed it to Stanwick.

Stanwick held the document gingerly and gave a low whistle.

"A letter from Churchill's private secretary to a John McMasters," he mumured. "Not a name I recognize. Probably a constituent. 'Sir Winston very much appreciates the book you sent him' and so on. Dated in mid-1950. Cream-colored paper. Letterhead refers to Chartwell, Churchill's country home. The valuable bit is the handwritten inscription 'With warmest good wishes, Winston S. Churchill' along the bottom after the secretary's signature. Only about a year and a half later, he returned to power as Prime Minister."

"Stephen is urging me to buy it," said Mrs. Bryant. "He is letting me keep it and look it over this week."

Stanwick smiled faintly.

"My advice," he said, "is to have nothing more to do with Mr. Faybush. In fact, I think I'll place a call to the local constabulary about him. This letter is a fraud. May I suggest that you find a good mutual fund for your money?"

How does Stanwick know the letter is a fraud?

Solution on page 161

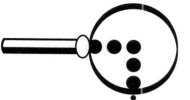

SOLUTIONS

The Case of the Wells Fargo Money (page 92)
Suppose Acker is lying. Then, from his second statement, he was out of town at the time of the robbery and Crowley is lying. If Crowley is lying, they are all using the lying code, including Barrington. If Barrington is lying, however, then Acker was in town at the time of the robbery. Thus, if Acker is lying, he was both in and out of town at the time of the robbery. This is impossible. Acker is therefore telling the truth.

Since Acker is telling the truth, he knows where the money is, and Barrington is using the lying code. Not everyone is using the lying code, so Crowley is telling the truth and doesn't know where the money is. Barrington may or may not know the location of the money.

A Slaying in the North End (page 95)
Neither Diskin nor Foster is the leader (4). Since the leader is married (3), he isn't O'Keefe (6), and since he plays poker Tuesday nights (4), he isn't Jensen either (2). The leader therefore is Lyons.

The leader and the killer are different men (1), so Lyons isn't the killer. Neither Jensen nor O'Keefe is the killer (5). Since the killer has a sister (5), he isn't Foster either (3). Therefore the killer is Diskin.

Bad Day for Bernidi (page 97)
Stanwick suspects Bernidi himself.

According to Bernidi's story, he lay down in the narrow space behind one of the display counters. His face was to the wall, and the lower wooden panels of the counter would have obstructed his vision even if he had turned. Since he supposedly did not arise until after the thief left, he could not have known that the thief used a burlap sack.

Business had been bad for Bernidi. He fabricated the entire robbery for the insurance money and was sent to prison for his trouble.

An Unaccoutable Death (page 99)
Morey said that he had touched nothing after finding Lombard in his lit office, yet when Walker arrived he had to snap on the lights. Morey

later confessed to killing Lombard after the accountant had found tax fraud and threatened blackmail.

The Case of the Purloined Painting (page 101)
Had an outsider broken the patio door glass to get in, the glass would have been on the floor inside, not out on the patio where Stanwick found it. The glass had therefore been broken from the inside.

The maid later confessed to being an accomplice in the theft, and both thief and painting were found.

The Week of the Queen Anne Festival (page 103)
All three are lying, and Thursday alone is a festival day.

If Chiswick's statement is true, then they are all liars, including Chiswick. He would thus be a liar telling the truth, which is impossible. Chiswick's statement is therefore false, and Chiswick is a liar. At least one clause of his compound statement is therefore false.

Since Chiswick's statement is false, Green's claim that it is true is also false, and Green is also a liar. Thus his other statement that Tuesday is a festival day is false. Hunter's first statement is false, since Chiswick and Green are both lying. Hunter is therefore also a liar, and Wednesday is not a festival day.

Thus, all three are liars. This means the first clause of Chiswick's statement is true. For the statement as a whole to be false, which it is, the remaining clause must be false, so Friday is not a festival day either.

Tuesday, Wednesday, Thursday, and Friday are the only possible festival days. Since at least one must be a festival day, and Tuesday, Wednesday, and Friday are not festival days, then Thursday must be the only festival day.

Death of a Con Man (page 105)
Cochran is the killer. There are several proofs, of which this is one:

The second statements of Cannon and Cochran contradict each other. Therefore one is true and one is false. Since each suspect is making one true and one false statement, the first statement of one of them, denying guilt, is true, and the other denial is false. Thus, one of them is the killer.

The killer cannot be Cannon, since both his statements would then be false. Therefore the killer must be Cochran.

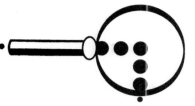

The Case of the Edgemore Street Shooting (page 107)

Kravitz said that Walder was approached from behind and shot before he could see his assailant. If this were true, Walder would have been shot in the back, not in the chest.

Kravitz was convicted of the murder.

Death Comes to the Colonel (page 109)

Since the colonel's phone rang, it must have been on the hook. According to George Huddleston, however, the colonel had had a sudden seizure while dialing, and nothing had been touched since. If this were true, the phone would have been dropped, and would not have been found back on the hook.

Huddleston was later convicted of poisoning the colonel for inheritance money.

Stanwick Finds the Magic Words (page 111)

All green elephants drink martinis at five (statement 6). But members of the Diagonal Club drink martinis only at four (3). Therefore no green elephants are members of the Diagonal Club. But only green elephants who are members of the Diagonal Club can wear striped ties (5). Thus no green elephants can wear striped ties.

All friends of winged armadillos, however, wear striped ties (1). Therefore no green elephants are friends of winged armadillos. But all who eat pickled harmonicas are friends of winged armadillos (4). Thus no green elephants eat pickled harmonicas. But only those who eat pickled harmonicas can enter a chocolate courtroom (2). Therefore (and these are the magic words) no green elephants can enter a chocolate courtroom.

The Great Watermelon Cover-Up (page 113)

Frank alone knocked over the melons.

Since Tommy is telling the truth, only one boy is the culprit. Harry is lying, so Tommy and Frank are not both telling the truth. This means Frank must be lying. Therefore Frank, and only Frank, knocked over the melons.

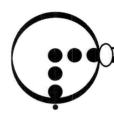

Inspector Walker Feels the Heat (page 115)

Ellis alone is guilty of assaulting the deputy mayor.

Suppose Chase is guilty. Then Heath is innocent (4). But then Decker is both guilty (1) and innocent (5), which is impossible. Therefore Chase is innocent. Since Chase is innocent, Mullaney is innocent (2). Therefore Heath is innocent (3). (If Heath were guilty, then Mullaney would be guilty, but Mullaney is innocent.) Since Heath is innocent, Decker is innocent (5).

Each member of the gang of four is therefore innocent. Since at least one of the five suspects is guilty, the guilty man must be Ellis.

Stanwick Visits Scotland Yard (page 117)

James Malcolm stole the documents.

If he and his wife had gone to the theatre, the ticket-taker would have kept half of each ticket he tore. Thus, when Malcolm carelessly produced both halves of two torn theatre tickets, his alibi was proved false.

The Explorer's Tale (page 120)

Justin mentioned seeing tigers in the African jungle. Africa has no wild tigers.

The Case of the Reindeer Spies (page 122)

"Dasher" can't be Cantrell, who vacations with him, or Bircham or Delmarin, who are single. Since he has never left the state, he can't be Ephesos either. Therefore "Dasher" is Abelardo. Similarly, "Donder" can't be the single Bircham or Delmarin. Since he has a brother, he can't be Ephesos. Therefore "Donder" is Cantrell.

The retired, worldly Ephesos cannot be the dissatisfied "Cupid" or the provincial "Comet." Therefore he is "Dancer." And the well-traveled Bircham cannot be "Comet," so he is "Cupid." Delmarin is "Comet."

Stanwick and the Accidental Thief (page 125)

When Stanwick walked by the ladies' coin purses earlier, he was able to observe the price tags, implying that they were on the outside of the purses. When Carpenter examined the coin purse carried out by Celia Leonard, however, he found its price tag tucked inside, where she had hidden it.

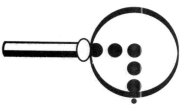

The McPherson–McTavish Mystery (page 128)

McTavish's golf bag is only scuffed. If he had dragged it across the moor to the knoll, as he claimed, it would also have had the moor's sticky red clay adhering to it, as it had adhered to Stanwick's shoes. The missing knife had nothing to do with the crime.

McTavish was convicted of murdering his neighbor over a land dispute and then attempting to frame McPherson.

Murder in a London Flat (page 131)

Since the gunman was not in London the week before the crime, he could not be Llewellyn, Merrick, or Halifax. Therefore the gunman is Cross. Neither Merrick nor Halifax, who kept the flat under surveillance, is the innocent bystander, so he must be Llewellyn.

Llewellyn knows Merrick, but not the lookout, so the lookout must be Halifax. Merrick, by elimination, must be the planner.

The Road to Trigoon (page 133)

The first and second men contradict each other by calling each other liars, and the third man supports the second man (Bruce). Therefore either the first man is lying and the other two are telling the truth, or the first man is telling the truth and the other two are lying.

If the third man were telling the truth and either road were fine, then the directional answers of the first two would be either both true or both false (depending upon whether their statements were considered exclusive). Since the first two contradict each other, the third man must instead be lying.

Therefore only the first man is telling the truth, and the road on the right is the road to Trigoon.

The Matter of the McAlister Murders (page 135)

If Collins's statement had been false, then Byran and Derrick would have been the guilty ones. Collins would then have been an innocent man telling a lie. Therefore Collins's statement was true, and he was innocent.

The other innocent one must have been either Byran or Derrick, as Collins stated. Therefore Addler was guilty and his statement was false, so Byran was innocent and Derrick was guilty. Addler and Derrick were therefore the guilty ones.

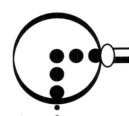

Death in the Garage (page 137)

If McCarthy had committed suicide, he probably would have taken the pills soon before succumbing to asphyxiation. Since the pills took effect so quickly, he would have had to take them while already seated in the car.

To take several large lozenges, however, he would have needed something to wash them down with, and no beverage container was found in the car. Stanwick therefore believes that the case is one of murder made to resemble suicide.

Murder at the Chessboard (page 139)

Rimbach's story implies that the murder occurred during a game of monochromatic chess. In this form of chess, the knight, a piece that moves only from a black square to a white square or from a white square to a black square, can never move.

In the position on the dead man's chessboard, however, a knight had moved to the center of the board. Rimbach is therefore lying. He committed the murder and then set the scene in the study, but in setting up the chess position made a fatal error.

The Norfolk Bank Robbery (page 141)

Kuhlman was not the shooter (1). Pickett was not the shooter either but, since he was involved, he was either the driver or the collector (3).

Schartner and Langley were not both involved, since in that case Brinner (2) and Pickett (3), one too many, would also have been involved. Therefore the driver was either Kuhlman or Schartner (4). Pickett must therefore have been the collector.

Langley could not have been involved at all, since that would have required the involvement as well of Brinner, Kuhlman or Schartner, and Pickett, again one too many. So the shooter must have been either Brinner or Schartner. The driver could not have been the pool-playing Kuhlman (5, 1), so he must have been Schartner. The shooter must therefore have been Brinner.

The Scottish Servants (page 143)

Since the average age of the butler (Jermyn) and the chief gardener (Harding) is 51, their combined ages must be 102. Harding is also 12 years younger than Jermyn, so Harding is 45 and Jermyn is 57.

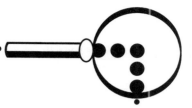

Mrs. Morgan, being three years older than Harding, is 48. She is also 20 years older than Mollie, so Mollie is 28. When Mrs. Morgan was the age Mollie is now (20 years ago), she was 28. At that time she was four times as old as Nellie, so Nellie then was 7. Nellie's age now is therefore 27.

The Case of the Purloined Presents (page 146)
The thief must be one of the three who left since the sack was last seen. Brennan's bad back prevented him from carrying a 30-pound (66 k) sack. Since no bags or bundles are unaccounted for, McNutt must have carried out his backpack and his two suitcases, which would have made his hands too full to carry a sack as well. Hunter came in with only a backpack, however, and so could have carried the sack out. He must be the thief.

The Case of the Three Confessors (page 149)
The third statements of Barrows and Connor are identical, so they must either both be liars or both be truth-tellers. They cannot both be truth-tellers, since Connor's second statement contradicts Barrow's first statement. Therefore they are both liars.

This means that their confessions are false, and neither was involved in the theft. Since Connor's second statement is false, but Barrows was not involved, Appleby must have committed the theft alone.

Since Appleby is a truth teller, the mace was stolen either late Wednesday afternoon or Wednesday night. The third statements of Barrows and Connor are false, so it was not stolen late Wednesday afternoon. The mace was therefore stolen Wednesday night.

Blackmail at City Hall (page 151)
The envelope was addressed only to "Deputy Mayor," and yet without even opening the envelope, Blair knew which deputy mayor to send it to.

The Churchill Letter (page 153)
The letter was dated in 1950 and refers to "Sir Winston", but Churchill was not knighted (thereby earning the use of the title "Sir") until 1953.

WHODUNIT -YOU DECIDE!

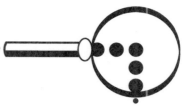

OPENING STATEMENT

I love a twisty mystery—the locked room, the impossible crime, the pivotal piece of evidence that appears to make no sense even though it has to. I love it when the writer plays with my mind, but plays fair. I love to slowly turn the story inside out and finally discover that elegantly simple twist that once made the author laugh out loud and say, "They'll never untangle this one."

The traditional "whodunit" does not hinge on police techniques, trivia, or even pure logic. It is based on imagination, and I'm often disappointed at how few real whodunits are being written these days. Arthur Conan Doyle, Agatha Christie, and Ellery Queen, the masters of the genre, were always clever and never too annoyingly complex.

Whodunit—You Decide! is my attempt to revive a taste of this classic form. All twelve of these murder mysteries, unraveled in the courtroom, share the same premise. Someone stands accused of a crime. And it is up to the jury—you the readers—to untangle the evidence and to find the defendant guilty or not guilty. Of course, as you'll discover, it's never that simple. There's always a twist. Was the murder a frame-up? Was it an accident? Was a suicide made to look like murder? Or did something even more devious happen?

Begin by reading one of the court cases in this book. Consider the "Trial Witnesses & Evidence" section at the end of the story, and note the minimum number of clues required to reach an informed verdict. Choose from the five possibilities which piece(s) of evidence you'll review first. Examine the clues one at a time, and try to digest each clue before you consider the next.

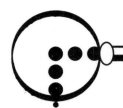

Very few readers will be able to solve a case and reach a verdict in the recommended minimum number of clues. Most readers will need to wade through all five pieces of evidence before going into deliberation. In the "Jury Deliberations" section you, as a member of the sitting jury, must review the evidence and try to make sense of it. If your budding theory fails to address all the concerns debated in jury deliberations, then return to the account of the crime and the evidence. Take your time in reviewing the case, and try to tie up all loose ends before you finally look up the solution in the "Verdicts" section.

Classic whodunits rank among the purest forms of puzzle; they ask you to make delicious sense out of what's seemingly contradictory. So, please relax and enjoy them. Devising these devilish twisters demanded a lot of hair-pulling and laughing out loud. I hope you'll have just as much fun solving them as I had creating them.

Hy Conrad

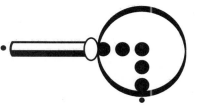

OUR MAN IN THE FIELD

At 9:08 P.M., a silent alarm rang at Ajax Security Co., sending an armed guard to the midtown branch of First National Bank. When he arrived on the scene, the guard discovered masked men scooping $20 bills out of the automatic-teller machines. One of the burglars physically attacked the guard, getting his own mask torn off in the fight and revealing his face to the bank's video system.

Somehow the guard managed to pull his gun and shoot, hitting his adversary squarely in the chest. The second burglar dropped the money and went to his bleeding partner's aid. He dragged his injured friend into a light-colored car hidden in the nearby alley. Both bank robbers escaped.

About 7 miles away, a pair of workmen from the water department had just finished restoring service to a rural neighborhood. "The water was off for about an hour," the senior technician later told the police. "We got it running at about 8:55, then stopped for a cup of coffee. We were just heading back when Mike spotted this guy in a field. It was a full moon and we could see he was dragging something through the weeds. We pulled over to see if he needed help. And then we saw the body. He was dragging this dead, bloody body. This guy was little and didn't have a gun. So Bill held him while I phoned the police. That was like 9:25."

"We arrived at 9:31," Officer Brill explained. "The man identified himself as Wally Heath. The body had a bullet in its chest, but Mr. Heath didn't have any explanation to offer. He invited us into his house. Mr. Heath, as it happens, lives right beside the field. The house was furnished nicely but kind of messy. He said his wife had recently left him, run off with some traveling salesman. He seemed more preoccupied with telling us about his domestic situation than about this body. We were there for maybe 10 minutes. Just before we took him in, the washing machine timer went off. We went with him to check it and saw the clothes in the washer were kind of dingy, like they'd been

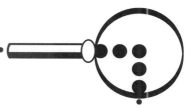

sitting in dirty water. We advised him not to touch them, just in case there might be some evidence. Then we read him his rights."

When the case came to trial, Wallace Heath stood accused of robbery, not murder. The corpse he had been dragging through the field has been identified as the late Judd Okan, a career criminal with a rap sheet in burglary and larceny. Computer-enhanced "stills" from the surveillance camera identified him as the unmasked burglar shot by the security guard. A still of the other robber remained unhelpful. Although the masked image did resemble Wally Heath in general size and build, it also resembled hundreds of other local men.

In court, Wally Heath's attorney seems at a loss.

DEFENSE: My client has absolutely no criminal record. He has lived in this town for 8 years, held the same job for 7 and was married to the same woman for 12. Although the Heaths were not a particularly sociable couple, Mr. Heath has been known to be a law-abiding man with the patience of a saint. He was at home the entire night in question, watching TV and doing his laundry.

True, Mr. Heath is not willing to tell us how he happened across Judd Okan or why he was dragging the body through the field behind his house. But it is not the Defense's job to establish Wally Heath's innocence. Rather, it is the Prosecution's job to establish his guilt, something they will be unable to do.

You and your fellow jurors are also at a loss. If Heath is so innocent, then why won't he explain his incriminating behavior?

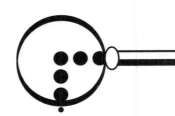

Trial Witnesses & Evidence

This crime can be solved with 2 clues.

Evidence Secured in Field

OFFICER: The field covers about 2 acres. Bordering the field on two adjacent sides is a road that swings around. On the third side is the Heath house and on the fourth is an abandoned well with a patch of woods behind it. The tall weeds left good impressions. It was easy to spot the path of trampled weeds. It appeared that a body had been dragged from the road into the middle of the field. We found the body about midway along this path. It was face up, the feet pointing toward the road.

PROSECUTION CROSS-EXAMINATION: What makes you think this path had been made by the dragged body?

OFFICER: We found blood and fibers along the entire path. They all match those of Judd Okan.

Prosecution Exhibit C, Autopsy Report

AUTOPSY REPORT: Cause of death was a single gunshot wound to the chest. The bullet entered the thorax cavity between the third and fourth ribs, causing a collapsed lung and piercing the septum wall between the left and right ventricles. Death occurred within 5 to 10 minutes.

PROSECUTION: Was the bullet in Mr. Okan fired from the handgun belonging to the Ajax Security Co. guard?

DEFENSE OBJECTION: The medical examiner is not a ballistics expert.

The Prosecution's next witness, a ballistics expert, testifies that the bullet did indeed come from the security guard's gun.

Evidence from Car

DEFENSE: Officer, please describe the car that was parked by the field.

OFFICER: It was a tan Toyota registered to the defendant. It was parked on the road beside the path of trodden-down weeds. The Toyota's

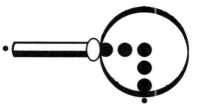

trunk was open and inside was a shovel. No dirt was visible on the shovel or in the trunk; so, we assumed the implement had not been used recently.

PROSECUTION: Was Mr. Heath's car searched for blood, fiber, hair, dirt, etc.?

OFFICER: Yes, it was.

PROSECUTION: And the results?

OFFICER: There was no blood of any kind. No dirt or vegetation. We did find several hairs matching the defendant's and fibers matching his clothes. Also, several unidentified hairs and fibers. But we found nothing at all matching the late Mr. Okan.

Laundry Analysis, Defense Witness

The Defense introduces a chemist who analyzed the dirty clothing in Wally Heath's washing machine.

CHEMIST: I started by comparing the dirt in the washer to soil samples from the field.

DEFENSE: And the result?

CHEMIST: No match.

DEFENSE: Were you ever able to match the dirt samples from the clothes?

CHEMIST: As a matter of fact, yes. I discovered from the county that there had been a water-main break that evening. When the water was turned back on at 8:55, it ran dirty for the first several minutes. If Mr. Heath had started the wash cycle at 8:55 or soon after, he would have filled the machine with that dirty water. The samples match perfectly.

Evidence from Defendant's House

DEFENSE: Did you examine the house for clothing?

INVESTIGATING OFFICER: Yes, and we found nothing resembling the light-colored jumpsuit worn by the masked perpetrator.

DEFENSE: Would you expect the perpetrator's clothing to have blood on it?

INVESTIGATING OFFICER: Yes. Judd Okan was bleeding heavily. The other man would certainly have gotten it on himself.

DEFENSE: And did you find any blood at all in Mr. Heath's house?

INVESTIGATING OFFICER: We did.

DEFENSE: What? You did?!

INVESTIGATING OFFICER: Yes. We ran over the entire house with phosphorescent light, designed to reveal the smallest traces of blood. We found blood residue on the floor of the laundry room and the kitchen and trailing out into the field.

The Defense appears devastated by this revelation.

THE HAUNTED HOUSE MURDER

The Prosecutor paced in front of the jury.

PROSECUTION: It all began as a harmless escapade.

Four healthy teenagers sneaking into an old abandoned house. A final night of adventure before one of them went off to college. That will never happen now. Lilly Kincaid will never go to Princeton. For on that night, Lilly was brutally murdered by this man, William Willis.

Even dressed up in a cheap suit paid for by his lawyer, Billy Willis looked like the homeless recluse he was. Harmless enough, or so everyone had thought.

The prosecutor reviewed the facts. The trespassing teens had been Lilly Kincaid, her younger sister, Anne, and their boyfriends, Mark and Larry. On a sultry August night, a week before Lilly's departure for Princeton, all four finally did what they'd always talked about, breaking into the eerily isolated Alway mansion at midnight and searching for ghosts.

Lilly's boyfriend, Mark, had been in the lead, using his flashlight to illuminate cobweb-filled crannies. Despite promises to the contrary, the boys were having their fun, scaring the girls at every opportunity. They had finished exploring the first floor and were halfway down a second-floor corridor when Larry turned around and saw that Lilly was no longer behind him.

"Lilly? Where are you?" Their whispers grew louder as they began to backtrack along the corridor. "Stop fooling around." Lilly was hardly the type to wander off on her own. "Lilly?" And then they heard it. Several muffled shouts followed by a piercing scream. Lilly's scream.

When Anne and the boys stepped into the dusty bedroom, they saw the 18-year-old stretched out on the bed frame. A hunting knife was protruding from her chest, the black handle-grip facing her shoes.

174

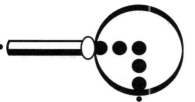

They were hoping it was all a perverse joke, Lilly getting even with the boys. Anne nudged her sister, telling her to cut out the dramatics. "Lilly?" Anne gazed down at her own hands. They were covered in blood. "She's... she's dead."

Mark was just stepping forward to check her pulse when Anne gasped. "Oh, my God. Did you see?" She pointed out into the hallway. "A man with a knife."

Instinctively, the boys gave chase, inadvertently leaving the surviving sister alone. No more than 30 seconds later, as they pursued clouds of cobwebs through the downstairs rooms, a second scream brought them up short. "Anne!" Mark and Larry instantly reversed their tracks.

"You left me alone!" Anne screamed as they ran back in. "Let's get out of here." The boys agreed. Whoever had done this was still close by, wielding a second knife. They ran, Anne sandwiched between her protectors, and didn't stop until they'd reached the safety of the police station.

When Ben Alway, the mansion owner, was told of the murder, his opinion was unequivocal. "Billy Willy," he replied. "Willis, I mean. A homeless drunk who's been squatting in the house for years. I kick him out and lock up the place, but he always finds some way in. The girl must have surprised old Billy. He's got a crazy, violent streak. Anyone'll tell you."

An hour later, the police discovered the lanky, middle-aged drunk passed out in the park. He had finished two pints of bourbon and his hand was gripped around a third. Through his alcoholic stupor, Billy denied the murder. "I ain't been in that place for days. That Alway guy is crazy. Last time, he took a shotgun and put it right up to my head. Said he'd blow my brains out if I ever came back."

Anne Kincaid was unable to identify Billy Willis in a line-up, but there still seemed to be more than enough evidence. The district attorney summed up his case with an emotional appeal.

PROSECUTION: Lilly Kincaid was the proverbial golden girl, the joy of her family, the focus of their hopes and dreams. For years Lilly's parents struggled so that one of their children could go to a good college. And now those hopes and dreams...where are they? Stabbed through the heart by a drunken monster.

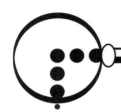

Trial Witnesses & Evidence

This crime can be solved with 3 clues.

Prosecution Witness, Ben Alway

The Prosecution calls Ben Alway to testify about his meeting with Billy Willis on the day of the murder.

The short, unassuming man says he never threatened Willis with a shotgun and that Willis, a vagrant, appeared edgy and desperate for a drink. During Defense cross-examination, Alway states that on the night of the murder he was at home, 2 blocks away, alone, watching television. The Defense questions Alway about his connection to the victim. Alway teaches at the local high school.

BEN ALWAY: I never had Lilly in any regular class. But in the summer, I work with students, preparing them for college boards. Last year, I coached Lilly, and this summer, Anne was in my group. Now that Lilly is dead, the Kincaids are hoping Anne will get into Princeton.

Defense Witness, Clerk

Vincent Winters, a clerk at All-Nite Liquor, testifies that at approximately 11 P.M. on the night of the murder, Billy Willis entered his store and bought 3 pints of Retcher's bourbon.

VINCENT WINTERS: He paid in loose change, like always. During the day Billy panhandles along Oak Street. Every now and then he makes enough to splurge on bourbon.

The Defense introduces this testimony in an attempt to strengthen the defendant's alibi, that he had been drunk and in the park at the time of the murder.

Police Crime Scene Report

SERGEANT JACKSON (*referring to his notes*): It was a single, fatal blow, delivered in a downward thrust, the handle-grip turned up in the fingers for a better grasp. We have yet to determine ownership of the weapon. The defendant's prints were found in six different locations around the room.

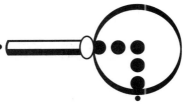

During Defense cross-examination Jackson admits he found no prints on the weapon.

DEFENSE: Isn't it odd for a killer to carefully wipe off the knife and yet leave his prints all around the room?

SERGEANT: Maybe.

DEFENSE: Could the defendant have left his prints there a day earlier? Even a week earlier?

SERGEANT JACKSON: I suppose.

DEFENSE: Did any of the defendant's prints contain traces of the victim's blood?

SERGEANT JACKSON: No.

Forensic Blood Report

Under cross-examination, the police expert admits that more than one blood type was found at the scene.

POLICE EXPERT: Our initial sampling produced only one, a type matching the decedent's. A later sample taken from the shirt, however, revealed a secondary blood source. According to tests, this was animal blood, probably chicken.

DEFENSE: Do you have any idea how chicken blood might have gotten to the scene of the crime?

POLICE EXPERT: No idea at all. Unless the lab made a mistake. It happens.

Defense Exhibit A, the Second Knife

A hunting knife, identical in make to the murder weapon, was discovered lodged in the branches of a tree not far from the window of the room where the murder victim was found. Most of the knife's 6-inch blade had been broken off, leaving only a 3/4-inch steel shaft. The blade was never found. The second knife had been wiped clean, but a microscopic examination revealed traces of blood on the broken shaft. Lab analysis verified that this was animal blood, probably from a chicken.

The Defense introduces the knife as contradictory evidence, but suggests no plausible theory about how the knife blade had been broken or where the blood came from.

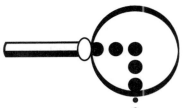

A WITLESS EYEWITNESS?

Alice Gabriel was a lonely woman who liked to use her binoculars to observe the world from her living-room window. Then one afternoon, while scanning the building across the street, Alice got more than she bargained for. Her statement was read in court.

ALICE GABRIEL: Several weeks ago, two unsavory-looking men moved into the dilapidated house directly across from my place. A tall, thin man and a short, fat one, like the Mutt and Jeff characters you read about in crime books. Sometimes a third man would come over. He looked different, nice and mild-mannered. All three often talked or played cards. Sometimes the nice-looking man took notes in a little notepad.

Well, on this particular Sunday, the nice man came to visit again. Only the short fellow was at home and he seemed very drunk. They talked for a while, then got into some sort of argument. All of a sudden the short man pulled out a tiny silver gun and started waving it around. The nice man managed to grab it from him. Then they moved out of my line of sight and I had to change windows. I heard the shot. It wasn't very loud. At the next window, I refocused my binoculars. The short man was grabbing his chest and falling, blood all over his shirt. The nice man was holding the gun. He looked stunned. This was about 5:25 P.M.

A few seconds afterwards, the tall guy came home. He and the killer tried to revive the short guy, but you could tell he was dead. Then the two guys closed the blinds; so, I couldn't see anymore. I ran right into my bedroom and called the police. Believe it or not, I was put on hold for 10 full minutes before someone took down my information and another 7 minutes before a patrol car arrived.

According to police, the body of Sol "Little Sonny" Walker was discovered a half-hour later, not in the house itself but two blocks away, in an alley behind a neighborhood bar. Based on Alice Gabriel's testi-

mony, the mild-mannered man, Wade Poe, was arrested. A nitric acid test showed that he had recently fired a gun. The tall man of the trio, Busby Berkoff, was arrested as an accessory after the fact, for trying to help Poe cover up the crime and dispose of the body.

The district attorney expected the Defense to enter a plea of self-defense or accidental homicide. But the defendant surprised everyone by claiming total innocence. As the Defense begins its opening argument, you immediately see its line of attack—the credibility of the case's eyewitness.

DEFENSE: Alice Gabriel is a woman desperate for attention and blessed with a vivid imagination. Just look at the holes in her story. She says the victim was wearing a white T-shirt, yet his body was found in a brown dress shirt. She says he was killed by a small silver pistol, yet forensic evidence will show the murder weapon to be a .45-caliber weapon, a much larger gun which was never found. Even her statement on the time of death is wrong. Alice Gabriel says the shot occurred at 5:25. Yet we will produce two other witnesses who set the time of the shot at 5:40. Most important of all, Miss Gabriel says Sol Walker was shot in his house. Yet the police's own evidence proves that his murder took place in the alley behind McGregor's bar. Ladies and gentlemen, after hearing all the evidence, you will have no choice but to disregard Miss Gabriel's testimony and find my client not guilty.

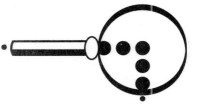

Trial Witnesses & Evidence

This crime can be solved with 2 clues.

Defense Witness, McGregor's Bartender

BARTENDER: At about 5:35 P.M., Busby Berkoff walked in and ordered a double of my best scotch.

DEFENSE: Did he seem upset, like his friend had just been shot?

BARTENDER: No. He was in a great mood, happier than I seen him in awhile. He and Sol live nearby. They'd been depressed lately on account of their shaky finances.

DEFENSE: And when did you hear the gunshot?

BARTENDER: About 5:40. Busby and I both heard it. I couldn't leave the bar and Busby didn't feel safe checking it on his own. This ain't the best neighborhood. So, we called the cops.

Defense Witness, Mrs. Wade Poe

MRS. WADE POE: Wade first met Sonny and Busby at McGregor's bar. Normally, Wade would never associate with that type, but Wade is a novelist. He's writing a book about low-lifes and con artists and wanted it to sound authentic. That's why he befriended them— for research.

PROSECUTION CROSS-EXAMINATION: Are you aware that at 5:32 on the day of the murder, your husband went to the bank beside McGregor's bar and withdrew $10,000?

MRS. WADE POE: That's what the police say.

PROSECUTION: Do you know why he withdrew it?

MRS. WADE POE: No.

PROSECUTION: Do you know what happened to the money?

MRS. WADE POE: No, I don't.

PROSECUTION: Could he have used it to buy Busby Berkoff's silence?

DEFENSE: Objection.

JUDGE: Withdraw the question.

PROSECUTION: Does you husband own a gun, Mrs. Poe?

MRS. WADE POE: He used to own an old Colt .45. I don't know what happened to it. Wade says it was stolen.

Police Chemist

PROSECUTION: Did you perform a nitric acid test on the defendant?

POLICE CHEMIST: Yes. It showed that he had recently fired a gun.

PROSECUTION: Did you perform the test on anyone else?

POLICE CHEMIST: Yes. On the deceased, Busby Berkoff, Mrs. Wade Poe, the bartender, and Ms. Gabriel.

PROSECUTION: The results?

POLICE CHEMIST: Minute traces of nitrates were found on the deceased's right hand and in his right trouser pocket. Nothing on the others.

DEFENSE CROSS-EXAMINATION: Is it possible to pick up gunpowder traces if you simply handle a fired gun, without actually firing it yourself?

POLICE CHEMIST: Yes, but...

DEFENSE: Can gunpowder nitrates be washed off?

POLICE CHEMIST: If you wash thoroughly, yes.

DEFENSE: And if the assailant were wearing gloves?

POLICE CHEMIST: Then, of course, there would be no nitrate traces at all.

Prosecution Witness, Forensic Expert

PROSECUTION: You examined evidence from both scenes. Please summarize your findings.

FORENSIC EXPERT: In Mr. Walker's living room, we used a phosphorescent scope and found no blood traces. Nor was there any other evidence indicating a crime had taken place. In the alley behind the bar, we found quite a bit of blood, all matching the deceased's. The spatter patterns indicate the body had not been moved and that this was the scene of the crime.

DEFENSE: Here is the report of the first officer to arrive at Mr. Walker's home. Please read this section out loud.

FORENSIC EXPERT (READING): "The room was stuffy, and when I first entered I smelled a little gunpowder."

DEFENSE: Do you still insist there was no evidence of a murder having been committed there?

FORENSIC EXPERT: Yes. The officer was undoubtedly mistaken.

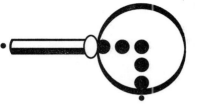

Autopsy Report

MEDICAL EXAMINER (READING): "Mr. Walker was killed by a single shot entering the chest cavity just below the sternum. His assailant had been facing him, approximately 8 feet away. The bullet we retrieved was from a .45-caliber handgun. Death occurred within seconds."

PROSECUTION: Was the physical evidence more consistence with an act of self-defense or with cold-blooded murder?

MEDICAL EXAMINER: Impossible to tell. We certainly found nothing to indicate that Mr. Walker had been threatening his assailant. But I really can't draw any conclusions.

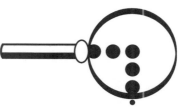

DEATH & THE SINGLE GIRL

Paul Gruber had been living in Casanova Towers for about two years and something always seemed to be going wrong. When he came home from work Tuesday evening, his new roommate was in the bathroom mopping up a puddle of water. "It started 15 minutes ago," Archie explained. "I pounded on the door of the apartment upstairs. No one's home. And the doorman's not answering the intercom."

Paul looked up at the bathroom ceiling. Water was dripping between the seams of the cheap acoustic tiles. "Ginger Mint's apartment."

"Didn't she give you a key for emergencies?" Archie asked.

"Yeah. I hope nothing's wrong."

Paul and Archie walked up one flight. Paul knocked on the door, then finally flipped through his keys, finding the one labeled Ginger.

"Inside her place it was deadly quiet," Paul later told the police. "Archie turned one way, to the bathroom. I turned the other, to the bedroom. Ginger's body was behind the bed; so, it took me a little while to see it. I called out. As soon as Archie came and saw the blood, he started to heave. He was heaving so hard he popped a button on his shirt. Archie wanted to look around for it, but I said no.

"On the way out of the apartment, I heard water running. I went into the bathroom and turned off the sink taps. I know I shouldn't have touched anything, but I didn't want the flooding to get worse."

Ginger Mint had moved to town 6 months ago and became involved with Todd Iona, a movie projectionist. On the day of the murder, Ginger told a coworker that she was nervous. Her boyfriend was going to drop over that evening. She was hoping to end their tempestuous relationship once and for all and wasn't sure how he would react.

Todd Iona is sitting at the Defense table as the Prosecutor previews the case against him.

PROSECUTION: We will introduce witnesses who will testify to Mr. Iona's jealous rages. Indeed, the victim told friends they were going to be meeting that night and she was afraid. Iona arrived at

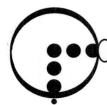

Ginger's prepared for murder. It took him only a minute to do it, using a knife from the kitchen. We will show how, after brutally stabbing her to death, Iona set up the bathroom sink to overflow, knowing that this would cause the body to be discovered. And why did he want it discovered so quickly? Because at that particular moment Todd Iona had an alibi.

Mr. Iona, you see, was a projectionist in a movie theater only a few steps from Casanova Towers. Between changing reels, he had 20 minutes, plenty of time to sneak out and run through the apartment tower's rear entrance, using the key Ms. Mint had given him just a month before. Minutes later, he was back in the privacy of his booth, where he had another full hour before his break, all the time he needed to clean up and dispose of his bloody clothing.

DEFENSE *(sarcastic):* What bloody clothing? Was any blood at all found in the projection booth or on my client? No. Ms. Mint did not ask my client to her apartment that evening. Why would she? He was working. No one saw him leave the theater or enter Casanova Towers. And as for having access, so what? The doorman had keys to her apartment. So did her downstairs neighbor. All the Prosecution has is the hearsay of a friend who said Ms. Mint was meeting her boyfriend. Is that enough evidence to convict a man of murder? I think not.

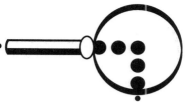

Trial Witnesses & Evidence

This murder can be solved with 2 clues.

Officer on Scene, Bedroom

OFFICER: No liftable prints, other than Ms. Mint's, were obtained from the bedroom.

PROSECUTION: Did anything in the bedroom catch your attention?

OFFICER: We discovered a white button on the rug between the body and the wall. This proved to be from Archie Gill's shirt. In addition, we found a photograph, a torn photograph. It was hidden behind a framed picture of Ms. Mint on the bureau. It showed Ms. Mint, presumably posed beside another person who had been torn out of the picture. We tried to trace it but haven't had any luck.

The partial photograph is admitted into evidence. It shows Ginger standing in the snow with a man's arm around her shoulder. In the background is a lighted Christmas tree.

Prosecution Witness, Ginger's Coworker

GINGER'S COWORKER: I met Ginger when she moved here in April, 6 months ago. She wasn't very talkative, but every now and then she'd mention Todd and how possessive he was.

DEFENSE CROSS-EXAMINATION: Did Ms. Mint say it was Mr. Iona who was coming over that night?

GINGER'S COWORKER: No. She just said "my boyfriend." She might have said "ex-boyfriend" once. I don't remember.

DEFENSE: So, she could have been expecting someone other than Mr. Iona.

GINGER'S COWORKER: I guess. Ginger didn't talk a lot about her love life.

Officer on Scene, Bathroom

OFFICER: Prints matching the deceased's were found all over the bathroom. Prints matching the accused's were found on the counter and mirror. A different set of prints was lifted from the sink's faucet handles. These were matched with those of Paul Gruber. A wad of

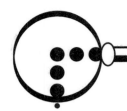

toilet paper had been stuffed into the sink's overflow drain, which forced the water to pour out onto the floor.

DEFENSE CROSS-EXAMINATION: If Mr. Iona had visited the deceased's apartment within the past few days, wouldn't you expect to find his prints in the bathroom?

OFFICER: Yes, I suppose so.

Prosecution Witness, Doorman

DOORMAN: Ms. Mint came in at 6:15 P.M. She said she was expecting a guest within the hour. I know Mr. Iona. She didn't mention him by name.

PROSECUTION: Did any guest arrive by the main door?

DOORMAN: No. And I was on the desk from 6:15 right up until 7:20. That's when Mr. Gruber called down and told me the police were coming.

DEFENSE CROSS-EXAMINATION: You were on the desk from 6:15 to 7:20?

DOORMAN: That's right.

DEFENSE: Mr. Gruber's roommate, Archie Gill, says he called the front desk at about 7:10 and no one answered.

DOORMAN: Well, I was there. Maybe I stepped outside in front for a smoke or something.

Prosecution Witness, Maintenance Man

PROSECUTION: Will you describe what you discovered in the garbage the morning after the murder?

MAINTENANCE MAN: Well, something was clogging the garbage chute. I went up floor by floor until I found the clog. It was between the fourth and fifth floors.

PROSECUTION: Ms. Mint lived on the fifth floor?

MAINTENANCE MAN: Right. Anyway, I found three large towels, all sopping wet. That's what was blocking the chute. On top of the towels was a pair of gloves. This particular hall chute runs right beside the murdered woman's apartment: so, I knew better than to touch anything.

The black leather gloves are admitted into evidence. They're men's large, the same size worn by the accused.

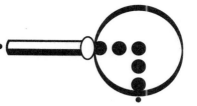

THE VANISHING VERROCCHIO

Lord George, the sixteenth earl of Brighton, had amassed one of the finest private collections of Renaissance art in Great Britain. A notorious recluse, the earl rarely ventured off his estate and hardly ever allowed outside eyes to view his priceless works. Like many collectors, he was obsessed with increasing his holdings. When it was announced that the Augustinian Fathers were considering selling their Verrocchio bust of St. Augustine, the earl jumped at the chance, claiming that he was prepared to offer more than any museum to acquire the statue, one of the few by Leonardo da Vinci's famous teacher to survive the centuries.

Late one afternoon, a black van drove through the gates of Brighton Manor, bringing the bronze St.Augustine for a formal appraisal and perhaps an informal offer. The earl of Brighton met his overnight guests at the door. Father Damien, a grim-visaged man, introduced himself. "Lord George, I must warn you. I am opposed to this transaction. The bust was a gift to our order centuries ago from the artist himself. To sell it would be a grave sacrilege."

The earl stood tall and unmoved. "That's your opinion. Don't tell me you drove the statue all the way here in that van? What about security?"

"The Lord is our security," Damien replied. "And Father Vito." He pointed to his companion, a priest about the same imposing size as himself but with a fierce scar running across one cheek.

The two friars carried a wooden crate through the hall and into the library and carefully unveiled the life-size bust. "Stunning" a voice whispered from the shadows. "Oh. Sorry to startle." A plump man waddled forward. "I'm Warren Tuffet, auction-house appraiser. Lord George brought me in to authenticate and advise. It's the Verrocchio, all right," he added after a minute's worth of inspection.

189

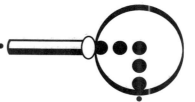

The foursome left the statue in the protection of an aging guard while the host led his guests on a tour. "The house has a Catholic background, you'll be pleased to hear. The second earl of Brighton was a devout Roman Catholic. During the reign of Henry VIII, he took in several priests, hiding them from the king's wrath. I assume you want to see my collection," he added reluctantly and showed them into the exhibition rooms.

When the museum tour was over, the host and his guests retired to refresh themselves and dress for dinner. It was during this break, while all were alone in different parts of the manor, that the crime took place.

At 7:17 P.M., the butler walked by the library and discovered the guard stumbling groggily about. The Verrocchio was missing from its wooden stand. Immediately, the servant sounded the alarm. Within minutes, the entire household had assembled. "Got hit," the guard mumbled, massaging a welt on the back of his head. "Knocked me down but not out. I saw..."

"Saw what?" Warren Tuffet demanded. "Who took the statue?"

The old guard, Edgar Chipping, didn't answer. He was too busy clutching his arm, then his chest, and then collapsing to the parquet floor under the impact of a massive heart attack. "Priest stole."

"Priest?" Lord George shouted. "Which priest? Both of them?"

"No." The guard shook his head in frustration, his face growing beet-red. "Priest stole." He pointed toward Father Damien standing by the spot where the statue had rested. "Here. Understand."

Those were to be the last words Edgar Chipping uttered. Within seconds he was dead, leaving Father Damien to face one count of grand larceny and one count of felony murder. The statue was never found and two months later the Augustinian was brought to trial, accused by the last words of a dying man.

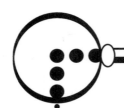

Trial Witnesses & Evidence

This crime can be solved with 2 clues.

Prosecution Witness, Security Chief
The earl's security chief describes Brighton Manor's antitheft precautions.

SECURITY CHIEF: The exhibition rooms are under constant video surveillance with several alarms spaced throughout, protecting the more valuable pieces. Unfortunately, there was no camera in the library, but we did have one focused on the manor's front door. It was operational at the time of the theft. As for the wall surrounding the grounds, it's made of smooth stone, 10 feet high and topped with barbed wire.

The videotape of the manor's front door is admitted into evidence.

Prosecution Exhibit A, Videotape
A videotape of the manor's front entrance reveals this: At 7:09 P.M., a tall figure dressed in an Augustinian friar's traveling robe with a hooded cape is seen exiting. Still photographs taken from the tape show that the figure is fully masked by his hood and robe and carrying a cloth sack filled with a heavy, bulky object.

There is no video record of anyone reentering the manor through the front door. The police assume that if the figure reentered the manor house, it was through another door. Several other doors had been unlocked at the time.

Officer at Scene
PROSECUTION: When you searched the area directly outside the grounds, what did you find?

OFFICER: Directly behind the west wall, the wall closest to the manor house, we discovered a large cloth sack, similar to the one in the video. Inside it was a hooded cape and a black robe.

PROSECUTION: Were you able to determine ownership of the robe?

OFFICER: It belonged to Father Damien—his traveling robe.

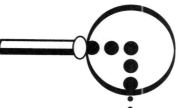

PROSECUTION: Do you have a theory of how the sack came to be found there?

OFFICER: Our theory is that Father Damien handed it over the wall to an accomplice who removed the statue, leaving the sack, robe, and hood.

DEFENSE CROSS-EXAMINATION: Why would Father Damien throw something as incriminating as his robe over the wall?

OFFICER: I don't know.

Defense Witness, Butler

DEFENSE: Was anything other than the Verrocchio statue missing from the library?

BUTLER: Yes, a Chinese pot. About 2 feet high. Fairly valuable. It had been standing in a corner of the room for years.

DEFENSE: Do you know what happened to the pot?

BUTLER: The police found it on the lawn, somewhere between the manor house and the west wall. It was still in one piece, thank heavens.

Statements of Whereabouts during Crime

LORD GEORGE: I was in my study, I had decided to make an offer on the Verrocchio and was calculating the range of my bid.

FATHER DAMIEN: I was in the guest room, in prayer. I was praying that the statue not be taken from us.

WARREN TUFFET: The butler will probably tell you I was sneaking around the upper floors. True. This was my first time inside the manor. Even though we had been given a tour, I was anxious to wander through at my own pace, appreciating the grand old house.

FATHER VITO: I was in my room on the phone. I was telephoning an old acquaintance in the city. I had heard a serious rumor regarding Lord George's financial solvency and asked my friend to do a little checking.

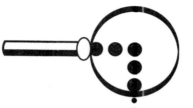

NO BRAKE
FOR THE WEARYS

The District Attorney points at the defendant, a handsome man in his twenties.

PROSECUTION: For years, Adam Weary had been living off his father's millions. And then the money dried up. Adam's new stepmother finally persuaded her husband to stop supporting Adam's spend-thrift ways. Adam's art gallery was in desperate need of funds in order to survive, money he could no longer get from his father. And that is why, on May 15, Adam Weary coldly planned and executed the double murder of his father and stepmother.

The Prosecution's case seemed solid. After the elderly executive George Weary married Pauline Gibson, the young beauty immediately took control of their finances, redecorating the hillside mansion and cutting off George's monetary outlays to his son.

Adam had tried many jobs during his young life: restaurateur, film producer, artist, and finally, owner of an art gallery. Each project had been lavishly subsidized by an indulgent father until Pauline came along. Despite this new development, Adam remained the secondary heir, inheriting the entire Weary fortune if both George and his new wife died.

According to the Defense's opening statement, Adam drove over to the hillside mansion on the morning of May 15 for breakfast. While there, Adam claims, Pauline asked him to change the oil in George's Cadillac. It seems the millionaire refused to go to the expense of a professional oil change and usually did the job himself. But Pauline was worried that George was getting too old for such exertion and might injure himself. Adam readily agreed, changing the Cadillac's oil and leaving the mansion at 11 A. M., just as a light, steady rain began to fall.

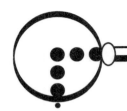

Adam's parting words were to remind Pauline about his gallery reception. He was counting on both of them to come that afternoon at 2. From the mansion, Adam drove straight to his gallery, where he remained until he was informed of the deaths.

At 5 P.M. Pauline's friend Sissy Yonkers dialed 911. "Something must have happened," she told the emergency operator. "Pauline was supposed to be at my place at 4 to go shopping. She's never late. She was going to drive here directly from the gallery, and her husband was going to drive to the airport to catch a business flight to Dallas. I telephoned his son's gallery. Neither one of them ever showed up. They've been missing for hours."

The 911 operator took down the report but did not share what he already knew, that the Wearys weren't missing, they were dead. At 1:30 that afternoon, George's Cadillac had flown through a guardrail and plummeted to the bottom of a ravine half a mile down the hill from the mansion. The plush leather and wood interior held the mangled remains of George and Pauline Weary. A later inspection of the vehicle showed that the break lines had been neatly severed.

Although fingerprints had been wiped clean from the area around the brakes, clear sets of Adam Weary's prints were found on other parts of the underchassis.

The district attorney concluded his opening statement.

PROSECUTION: Only Adam Weary had a motive; no one else profited from their deaths. Only Adam had opportunity; he was the only outsider admitted into the Weary home that morning. And although Adam will tell you his flimsy, unbelievable story about being asked to change his father's oil for the first time in his life, you will find that only Adam Weary had the means to commit these murders, since only his prints are to be found under the car.

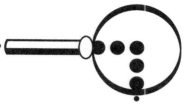

Trial Witnesses & Evidence

This crime can be solved with 2 clues.

Medical Examiner's Testimony

MEDICAL EXAMINER: Despite the airbags, both decedents were killed on impact. George Weary was in the driver's seat wearing a seat belt. His wounds were consistent with those expected: a broken neck and spine, other nonlethal fractures, and multiple contusions. Pauline Weary had not been wearing a seat belt. Her wounds also included a broken spine and were generally consistent with those expected.

On Defense cross-examination, the coroner admits that one of Pauline's wounds is not consistent with the crash: a severe open contusion on the back of her head. The ecchymosis (discoloration and swelling) indicates this wound had been inflicted before Pauline Weary's death. Also, white gravel fragments were imbedded in the wound.

The medical examiner also reported that the back of the decedent's dress was wet and dirty and contained white gravel fragments.

Police Crime Scene Report

A homicide detective testifies that no empty oil cans or other evidence of an oil change were found in the Weary's garage.

DEFENSE: What other findings can you report from your examination of the garage and the grounds?

HOMICIDE DETECTIVE: We found a patch of spilled oil on the garage floor in the spot where the Cadillac had been parked. The fingerprints of the accused were not found on the other car in the garage, Pauline Weary's Porsche. The brakes on the Porsche had not been tampered with. Blood was discovered on the white gravel path, halfway between the mansion and the garage. The gravel had been disturbed around that spot.

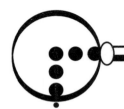

Defense Exhibit A, Prenuptial Agreement

The Defense introduces into evidence the prenuptial agreement between George and Pauline Weary, witnessed and signed a month before their marriage. In the document Pauline gave up all claims to community property and agreed, in the event of a divorce, to a lump settlement of $200,000.

The Defense introduced this evidence in an attempt to show that the Weary marriage was fragile from the beginning and unlikely to last.

Prosecution Exhibit C, George Weary's Will

Hoping to clearly establish a motive, the prosecution asked the Weary lawyer to read aloud the provisions of George Weary's will, drafted a week after his marriage. In the will, George Weary left the bulk of his estate to his wife, Pauline. In the event of her death before the will could be probated, Pauline's portion of the estate would revert to George's previous heir, his only child, Adam Weary.

Defense Exhibit B, Receipt from Car Interior

The Defense, in an attempt to establish an alibi for the time of the brake tampering, introduces a receipt found crumpled in the ashtray of the wrecked Cadillac. The receipt, for a quart of milk and a carton of cigarettes, is from a convenience store located at the bottom of the hill near the Weary estate. t was stamped at 11:48 A.M. on May 15, the day of the murder. The Defense uses this receipt to demonstrate that someone used the Cadillac after Adam left the house and that the brakes must have been in working order at that time.

The Prosecution introduces the salesclerk on duty at the convenience store at the time. She says she cannot remember either the sale or the car. The Prosecution claims that the receipt had been fabricated and planted in the Cadillac to provide Adam Weary with an alibi.

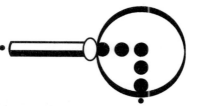

TRIAL OF THE BLACK WIDOW

For two months, the exclusive community of Palm Bay has been obsessed with a murder that many of its most influential citizens actually witnessed. You and your eleven colleagues feel lucky to sit here every day and weigh the evidence against this beautiful, and, some might add, deadly woman of the world.

It was less than a year ago that Anabel Lee moved to Palm Bay, renting a tastefully expensive beach house. A vivacious and stunning woman, Anabel quickly made friends, especially with Victor Ricolah, next-door neighbor and retired financier. They were engaged within two months, married within three. In his opening statement, the district attorney outlines the events of Victor's final garden party of the season, his last garden party ever.

The festivities were in full swing on that sunny afternoon when the host asked his wife to fetch him a drink. Anabel had just sent the bartender off for more limes; so, she made it herself, expertly mixing the gin and tonic and adding ice from an electric ice cooler plugged into an outlet in the gazebo. She tasted the drink, pronounced it delicious, then handed the glass to Victor, who used a paper napkin to wipe a red gash of lipstick off the rim before drinking.

That was the last contact that Anabel had with her husband. For the next half-hour, Victor sipped his drink, munched on a catered buffet of overpriced delectables, and chatted with his neighbors. At one point he borrowed a cigarette from his best friend and tennis partner, Keith Brown, but smoked only half before stubbing it out.

When Victor collapsed on the lawn clutching his throat, no one even imagined poison, except the poisoner of course. Three plastic surgeons and a dermatologist made vain attempts to revive him. And all this while the servants were busy washing glasses and disposing of whatever evidence might have existed of the murder.

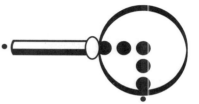

Anabel tried to arrange a quick cremation, but Palm Bay law required an autopsy. The result left no doubt: potassium cyanide, guaranteed to give effective results within a matter of minutes.

PROSECUTION: The Prosecution will show that last month Mrs. Ricolah drove to Boca Raton to purchase an industrial metal cleaner, a clear liquid composed primarily of potassium cyanide. We will also show that this was not the first time Anabel Lee Ricolah, born Amy Long, and also known as Annie Lyons and Andrea Leon, has lost a husband under suspicious circumstances. In at least two previous instances, she married wealthy men. In both of these cases, her husbands died within a year and in both cases their remains were cremated. Anabel Lee is what crime literature calls a "black widow," someone who weds and kills with impunity. It is your job, ladies and gentlemen of the jury, to see that her crime spree stops here.

    Anabel's lawyer was dismissive.

DEFENSE: There is no evidence connecting my client to this crime. So, she bought a metal cleaner. She likes a clean house. As for opportunity... cyanide is a fast-acting poison. And yet Mrs. Ricolah and her husband had no contact with each other for the last half-hour of his life. Other suspects abound. The Ricolah housekeeper, Emma Peters, had been the deceased's mistress for years before he threw her over for the defendant. The deceased's best friend, Keith Brown, had been an ardent suitor of Anabel's before the marriage. Both Emma Peters and Keith Brown had motives just as compelling as my client's and even greater opportunity.

You get the sinking feeling that no matter who poisoned Victor, there may not be enough evidence to prove it. Still, the question remains: Who killed Victor Ricolah? And How?

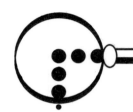

Trial Witnesses & Evidence

This crime can be solved with 2 clues.

Prosecution Witness, Toxicologist

TOXICOLOGIST: Luckily, Green Lady Catering uses distinctively colored garbage bags. We were able to recover all the party trash from the dump and sift through it. We limited ourselves to items Mr. Ricolah was observed ingesting. The videotape helped us in that regard. We also checked containers that might have held the poisoned item.

PROSECUTION: And what did you find?

TOXICOLOGIST: We found liquid traces of potassium cyanide inside a plastic food-storage bag—the kind with blue and yellow stripes on top. We also tested a tiny patch of dead grass near the spot where Mr. Ricolah collapsed. Again, we found minute traces of cyanide. In both cases, the chemical composition matched that of a common industrial metal cleaner.

DEFENSE: Objection. Information not asked for.

PROSECUTION: Were the traces of cyanide consistent with the ingredients of the industrial metal cleaner, Exhibit B?

TOXICOLOGIST: Yes.

Prosecution Witness, Housekeeper

Emma Peters, the Ricolah housekeeper, had helped the caterers clean up and was observed disposing of several food storage bags.

PROSECUTION: Do you remember what happened with the storage bags?

EMMA PETERS: As far as I can recall, I threw away three of them, all with those blue and yellow stripes on top. That's the kind Green Lady uses. I buy the same brand for the Ricolah household. One of the bags came from behind the buffet table. I think they were using it for parsley. The other two came from the bar area in the gazebo. One was used to store garnish items for drinks, and the other I found inside the electric ice cooler.

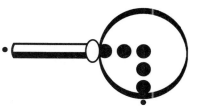

Prosecution Witness, Caterer

CATERER: Mrs. Ricolah's behavior seemed a little odd that day. For one thing, she insisted on doing many things our staff normally does, things like personally filling the ice cooler and stocking the garnish bins with lemons and limes and cherries. We tried to tell her, diplomatically, that we would take care of those details, but she insisted on doing them herself.

DEFENSE CROSS-EXAMINATION: Did you ever cater for the Ricolah household before?

CATERER: No.

DEFENSE: So, you never worked for Mrs. Ricolah before. In fact, that was the first time you ever met her.

CATERER: That's correct.

DEFENSE: So, you have no way of knowing what her normal behavior was and what might have been odd. In fact, she might normally be an independent person who likes to do things for herself.

CATERER: I suppose.

Cross-Examination, Toxicologist

DEFENSE: You've told the court where you found traces of poison. But where *didn't* you find traces?

TOXICOLOGIST: On everything else.

DEFENSE: You tested the paper napkin with the red lipstick smear? The lipstick tube? The cigarette butts? Dessert canapés? Drinking glasses?

TOXICOLOGIST: No, not the glasses. They had all been washed.

DEFENSE: But you tested everything else I mentioned?

TOXICOLOGIST: Yes.

DEFENSE: And the results of those tests?

TOXICOLOGIST: No trace of poison on any of them.

Defense Exhibit A, Party Videotape

Victor Ricolah had hired a video company to make a tape of the party, thereby ensuring a record of his own demise. By a lucky fluke, the videotape focuses on Victor in the minutes just prior to his death.

VIDEOTAPE: Victor is in the midst of his friends, nursing the last quarter of his gin and tonic. He stubs out his cigarette in an ashtray as Keith Brown deposits a plate of half-eaten food on a table and walks away. Victor absentmindedly eats a potato chip from the plate. Emma Peter passes by with a tray of dessert canapés. Several guests munch on the little sweets, including Victor. Halfway through his first bite, Victor clutches at his throat and collapses, dropping both the canapé and his glass on the lawn. The videotape continues to roll until the arrival of Mrs.Ricolah and the first doctor.

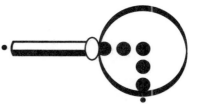

THE HOT DESIGNER

Vanushka Designs of New York was the hottest fashion house in the country. Its founder, Vera Vanushka, had led VDNY through eight spectacular years and was reaping the rewards by taking the company public in a sudden stock offering.

The delicate financial negotiations had been hindered by Vanushka's cold. She reportedly caught the bug one afternoon while walking on the beach during a thunderstorm. For several days, she stayed housebound in her Southampton mansion while Manny Moore, her chief financial offer, worked out details with the bankers. Despite her debilitating summer sniffles, the flamboyant designer kept in touch, driving Rose, her personal secretary, nearly crazy with an onslaught of faxes and memos to everyone in the company.

On Monday morning, VDNY made its debut on the stock exchange, soaring $20 from its opening price. But on that same evening a tragic, fatal fire took place and when the market reopened the next day, Tuesday, VDNY stock headed into a nosedive. Not only had Vanushka's charred remains been found among the ruins of her mansion, but Harve Grant, her brilliant assistant, had been arrested for arson and first-degree murder.

The Southampton courthouse was packed as the young, meticulously dressed defendant was led in. He hardly looked like a killer. But, as the prosecution pointed out, Harve certainly had a motive.

PROSECUTION: Harve Grant came to Vanushka fresh from the Fashion Institute. She took a chance with the unproven designer and was rewarded with three years of blockbuster collections. Vera Vanushka was certainly aware of Harve's value, and she made him a promise. Very soon, after the spring collection was shown, she would give him a share in the company. After all, Vanushka's financial officer had a piece, so did Rose, her longtime secretary. When VDNY finally went public, Harve could sell, growing rich with the rest of them. It was a promise Vanushka betrayed. And that betrayal led directly to her murder.

206

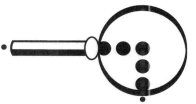

Harve slaved over the new collection, then flew off on vacation. On that fateful Monday morning, he was relaxing on a Mexican beach when he happened to glance at last Friday's *Wall Street Journal,* announcing the upcoming stock sale. Harve grabbed the first plane back to New York. and by that evening had arrived in the Hamptons. We do not know what transpired between Ms. Vanushka and the irate young man. But we do know the result. Harve knocked out the senior designer, left her in the kitchen, and then tinkered with the toaster oven. Five minutes after he left, when the appliance's timer went off, an electrical fire was ignited, fueled by a pile of newspapers on the counter. Harve was counting on the fire to make a cold-blooded murder appear like an accident.

DEFENSE: When my client arrived at the Vanushka home, naturally he was angry. No one answered the bell, the servants having been given two weeks off, so Harve broke a window and let himself in. He wandered around, but Ms.Vanushka didn't seem to be there. It never occurred to him to check the kitchen. His employer was hardly the domestic type. Ten minutes after arriving, at approximately 8:20 P.M., Mr. Grant drove away. Both his arrival and departure times have been documented by observant neighbors. Ten minutes. Hardly enough time to kill a person and arrange the elaborate electrical fire he's accused of having set up.

The evidence is circumstantial at best. The fire left no prints. No proof at all that he'd been in that kitchen. The prosecution cannot even establish the cause of death with complete certainty. For all we know, Ms.Vanushka may have accidentally set the fire herself, then died of a heart attack before she could escape. Stranger things have happened.

Your job is simply to find the defendant guilty or not guilty. Nothing more. But you can't help wondering what really happened that night in Southampton.

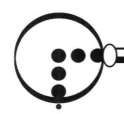

Trial Witnesses & Evidence

This crime can be solved with 2 clues.

Prosecution Witness, Ms. Vanushka's Secretary, Rose Clark

ROSE CLARK: I was in the office late that night. Ms. V. called about 8 P.M. She said she was at the house, but from the reception I could tell she was using her cellular phone. Ms.V. used that cell phone a lot. It was a designer model and she was partial to it.

PROSECUTION: Did Ms. Vanushka speak to anyone else?

ROSE CLARK: I'm sure other people in the office heard me talking to her, but no. Since her cold. Ms.V. communicated only through me or through Manny. I'm sure the phone company can supply you with the exact time of the call.

The Prosecution later produces records showing a call from Vera Vanushka's cellular phone to VDNY offices: 7:53 to 8:05 P.M.

Prosecution Witness, Fire Marshal

FIRE MARSHAL: We arrived on the scene at exactly 8:55. The fire was already out of control. I know all the mansions in the area, all the people, too. I called my office and asked them to get in touch with Manny Moore. I figured someone should be notified. He was having a dinner party at his house, maybe 10 minutes away. He came over immediately.

PROSECUTION: Can you describe the kitchen after the fire had been put out?

FIRE MARSHALL: Well, Ms.Vanushka was on the floor, lying on her back, approximately 5 feet from the counter where the toaster oven was situated. It was the most badly burned body I'd ever seen.

PROSECUTION: Did you find Ms.Vanushka's cellular phone anywhere in the room?

FIRE MARSHALL: Yes. We found the blackened remains of a phone right on top of the toaster. It was pretty well toasted—no pun intended. The representative from Nokia was able to identify the

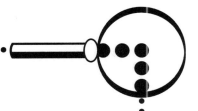

model—a custom-made design they'd done exclusively for Ms. Vanushka.

Prosecution Witness, Coroner

CORONER: The body was close to the blaze's center; so, there was a lot of damage. A surprising amount. Massive tissue damage, ruptured eardrums, severe nerve damage, as if they'd been fried. A broken femur. Even cataracts on both corneas. Vera Vanushka had literally been burned to death.

PROSECUTION: Then you would say she had definitely been alive when the fire started?

CORONER: Absolutely.

DEFENSE CROSS-EXAMINATION: For most fire victims, what is the cause of death?

CORONER: In most cases, it's smoke inhalation.

DEFENSE: But Ms. Vanushka didn't die of smoke inhalation; she was burned to death.

CORONER: Correct.

DEFENSE: Could the cause of death have been something other than the fire? Say, a severe electrical shock?

CORONER: Perhaps. But it would have to be extremely severe, more than you could ever get from a toaster oven.

Defense Witness, Phone Company Technician

DEFENSE: The charred cellular phone discovered in the kitchen—can you positively identify that as Ms.Vanushka's?

PHONE TECHNICIAN: The phone was a custom-designed Nokia. There are only two similar instruments in existence, one owned by the defendant and one owned by Manny Moore.

DEFENSE: So, you can't be positive that it was Ms. Vanushka's phone that was burned. It could have been Mr. Moore's or Mr. Grant's.

PHONE TECHNICIAN: Well, normally we can tell by the circuitry or the I.D. code. Both of these were obliterated in the fire.

DEFENSE: So, it could have been one of the other two phones burned in the fire. You really don't know.

PROSECUTION: Objection.

JUDGE: Where is this line of questioning headed?

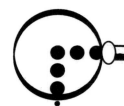

DEFENSE: The Defense merely wants to show that the call recorded as coming from Ms. Vanushka that night did not necessarily originate from the phone found in her kitchen.

Prosecution Exhibit A, Burned Umbrella

The Prosecution's case was damaged by the coroner's testimony. In the hope of emphasizing the intensity of the fire as the cause of death, the district attorney introduces a beach umbrella that had been stored in a closet just a few feet from the toaster oven. The metal frame is severely scorched, bent from the heat. A fire expert testifies that the umbrella could only have been reduced to that state by an intensely hot fire.

PROSECUTION: And, in your opinion, could such an intense fire kill someone before he or she died of smoke inhalation?
DEFENSE: Objection. Witness is not a medical expert.
JUDGE: Objection sustained.

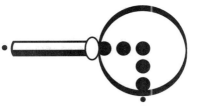

THE LADY IN THE DUMBWAITER

It was a chilly evening in March, 1930. England's legendary tycoon Lord Dudley was hosting a dinner party at his London mansion. As midnight struck, only the overnight guests remained, sipping their port and admiring the Asprey Whites, a collection of unset diamonds that had been passed down in Lady Dudley's family for generations.

"It will be a pity to sell them," Lady Dudley sighed. "But we do so need the money, at least until this stock-market thing turns around."

Lord Dudley protested that conditions were not that desperate. "How many times must I tell you, dear? I don't want you to do it."

"They're mine and I'm going to. I don't know why you're being so stubborn. Why, just last November, you were begging me to sell."

Marie Dudley was a sensible, good-natured girl, and she seconded her mother's feelings. "Don't keep them for my sake, Daddy. Enough of Gene's money survived the crash. If ever I need diamonds, I'm sure my future husband will provide."

Captain Eugene Batts held a family pedigree even more distinguished than the Dudleys'. "Within reason," the young aristocrat chortled. "Lucky for me, our Marie is not that fond of jewelry."

The fifth and final member of the group raised her voice in disbelief. "What? How can any woman not be fond of jewelry?" Katrina Burghar was Marie Dudley's best friend from school, as daring and full of life as Marie was drab and proper.

Lord Dudley stood by the window smoking his pipe. "What's that?" Suddenly he was gazing into the dark. "I saw something move. In the garden." Captain Batts joined him, and both men stared out into the darkness. "Someone was there, I tell you." The butler was sent out to check but reported that the garden was empty. Whatever had been out there was no longer around.

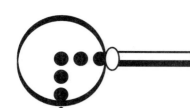

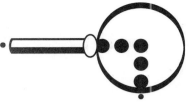

As the party broke up, Lord Dudley swept the diamonds into their velvet pouch. "I think I'll keep these in my bedroom. Better than the safe. Someone was definitely prowling around."

It was shortly after 1 A.M. when the first gunshot was heard. Lady Dudley emerged from her second-floor boudoir. Captain Batts came down from the third-floor guest bedroom and his fiancée ran up the stairs from the library. All three approached Lord Dudley's suite only to find the door locked.

A second gunshot thundered through the hall and was quickly followed by a dull thud. Mere seconds later, when Captain Batts shouldered open the door, they found Lord Dudley on the floor behind his desk. Dead—a bullet hole in his head. Clutched in his right hand was a fireplace poker. Marie noticed the open window and the brisk breeze. Captain Batts noticed the open desk drawer and the revolver lying in the bottom of it. But it was Lady Dudley who noticed the empty velvet pouch.

Exactly one month later, Lord Dudley's accused killer comes to trial. "Kat Burghar, the Deadly Cat Burglar," had been on every front page in Britain. You've seen her picture a hundred times. But sitting here in the defendant's box in His Majesty's court, she is even more attractive than you imagined. The Prosecution states its case.

PROSECUTION: Miss Katrina Burghar is a daring woman with a lust for precious gems. She was determined to get her hands on the Asprey diamonds and saw the dumbwaiter as the perfect means. This pulley-operated mechanism was used to lift food and plates from the basement kitchen to the dining room. It also opened on the second-floor master suite and on the guest bedroom above that. By squeezing her petite frame into this mini-elevator and pulling the ropes, Miss Burghar managed to lift herself unseen from the dining room to her victim's bedroom, where she killed her host, stole the diamonds, then retraced her route. If the family butler had not been in the dining room just as Miss Burghar emerged from the dumbwaiter, she might never have been caught.

Trial Witnesses & Evidence

This crime can be solved with 3 clues.

Defense Witness, Katrina Burghar

KATRINA BURGHAR: I did it as a lark—to see if I could really fit in and do it. If I got stuck, I figured I could always call out and either Lord Dudley or Captain Batts would hear me. There was no way I could get into their rooms by myself. The dumbwaiter door can only be opened from the outside.

DEFENSE: Please describe your experience.

KATRINA BURGHAR: I was in the dining room. Alone. I heard an odd noise, like something falling down the chute. When I first opened the dumbwaiter, the box was on the third floor, so I had to pull it down. Then I squeezed myself in and I began to pull up. I only managed to move a few feet and then... The first gunshot was terribly frightening. Right afterwards I heard some mumbling, like a man talking to himself. Then came the second shot and I lowered myself down. The butler was there when I came out.

PROSECUTION CROSS-EXAMINATION: Do you really expect us to believe you did this just as a lark?

KATRINA BURGHAR: It's the truth.

PROSECUTION: And what were you wearing for this rather athletic lark of yours?

KATRINA BURGHAR: Umm. I had changed into a black, sleeveless silk dress.

Prosecution Witness, Officer on the Scene

OFFICER: We assume it was the first shot that missed, since the witnesses described a heavy thud after the second. For the longest time we couldn't locate that first bullet. It was in the ceiling, clear across the room from the desk where the body was found. The desk's bottom right drawer was open about a quarter of the way. There were fresh scratches in the wood of the drawer's inside edge. These scratches match tiny slivers of wood on the sides of the revolver handle. The window was open, but there was no sign of an

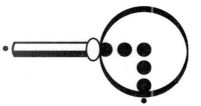

intruder. The door to the dumbwaiter was closed.

PROSECUTION: Can the dumbwaiter be opened from the inside?

OFFICER: No. But you can close it from the inside. The deceased could have opened it. As she left, Miss Burghar could have closed it.

PROSECUTION: Did you find Miss Burghar's prints in the room?

OFFICER: No. But we did find a pair of men's gloves beside the body. Traces of gun oil were on them.

Defense Cross-Examination, Officer on the Scene

DEFENSE: What did you find when you searched Miss Burghar's possessions?

OFFICER: Nothing. I mean we found no trace of the diamonds, neither on her person nor anywhere in the mansion or the garden.

DEFENSE: Did you find anything at all?

OFFICER: Yes. We found paste copies of the Asprey diamonds. Good imitations, too. They were in the bottom of the dumbwaiter chute.

DEFENSE: What made you search the dumbwaiter chute?

OFFICER: When we questioned Miss Burghar, she mentioned hearing something go down the chute.

DEFENSE: So, if she had not mentioned that noise, you might not have examined the chute?

OFFICER: We might have, eventually.

Prosecution Exhibit A, Revolver

The Prosecution introduces the murder weapon into evidence. A Scotland Yard firearms expert describes it as an American-made revolver, known to have been part of the deceased's gun collection, which he usually kept under lock and key in a downstairs display case.

FIREARMS EXPERT: There were no prints on the revolver, but we did find several fresh scratches on the trigger. Horizontal scratches, probably made by a hard metal object.

Coroner's Evidence

CORONER: He was killed by a single gunshot. The bullet entered the right jaw at a steep upward trajectory and lodged itself in the upper left hemisphere of the cerebrum. There was no evidence of a struggle.

DEFENSE CROSS-EXAMINATION: Assuming that the first shot missed its target, wouldn't you have expected to find evidence of a struggle?

CORONER: erhaps.

DEFENSE: Lord Dudley was in debt, yet he continued to maintain a generous life-insurance policy. Has Scotland Yard ruled out suicide?

CORONER: The evidence does not seem to support this possibility. The revolver was fired from 6 feet away and was found inside the drawer, several feet from the body. Also, at the time of his death, Lord Dudley had his gun hand occupied. He was holding a poker.

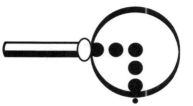

WILL-O'-THE-WISP

"A gunshot," Reggie Long yelled into the receiver. "And a split-second after that I heard a shout, a man's shout." He was still gazing out his living room window at the front of the house next door. "No one's come or gone. It's 412 Maple Street. Hurry."

The police dispatcher said a patrol car would be there within minutes, warning him not to leave his house. But Reggie's curiosity would not be denied. He slipped on his coat, grabbed a set of keys from a peg, and trudged out into a foot-deep carpet of newly fallen snow. Arthur, the neighbor from the other side of 412 Maple, was already standing at Gus's front door. "Arthur? Is anyone answering? I have a house key Gus gave me."

Arthur Ames pounded a fist on the door. "Gus?" he yelled, then tried the knob. "It's locked. Gus?" He waited several seconds, coatless and shivering. "OK. Give me the key."

The entry hall was dark as the neighbors stepped into the elegant house that separated their own residences. They didn't have to wander far to find the body. Gus Goode was lying in the doorway to his downstairs study, a pool of blood surrounding his head. Five feet away lay a .38 revolver. "Is anyone there?" a voice wailed from the second floor. "Something woke me. It sounded like... Is Gus all right? Gus?"

The neighbors knew the voice—Lydia, Gus's ailing bedridden wife. Before either could answer her or approach the corpse, the blare of a siren became audible, growing louder with each passing second.

Right off, the police noticed footprints. The snow had stopped a half-hour earlier and the white lawn of 412 was dotted with two clearly marked trails, one set leading from Reggie's house, the other from Arthur's, both trails converging on 412's doorstep. As expected, they found their suspect still inside. Joey Goode was Gus and Lydia's nephew, a deaf-mute who had been living with the elderly couple for the past year. When the police searched the third floor, they found Joey in his room watching the last of his morning shows on a soundless TV, seemingly unaware of the murder that had taken place just two floors below.

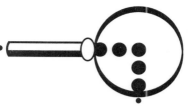

The alleged motive was found clenched in the victim's fist. Arthur, the family lawyer as well as neighbor, recognized the scrap of torn paper. "It's a corner of Gus's new will. He signed it last night. See here? The date. And part of the signatures of the witnesses, Reggie and me. I know it's not usual for a lawyer to witness a client's will. But Gus was insistent on getting it done right away. Lydia couldn't sign because she inherits."

Naturally, the police wanted to see a copy of the will. Arthur led the way to his own house. And that's where they encountered the day's second crime. "It's gone," Arthur said as he fumbled through his papers. "The only other copy of Gus's new will is gone. I put it in this file just last night."

No trace of either copy was ever found—not a shred, ash, or any other remnant—which made Gus's old will once again valid. The district attorney begins his opening argument.

PROSECUTION: Joey Goode had motive. He inherited under the old will, but not under the new. He was the only one with opportunity. No footprints other than the witnesses' were found in the snow. Also, the front door. It's not equipped with an automatic lock, which means that someone leaving the house could not simply pull the door locked behind him. He would have had to use a key. And yet the witnesses tell us the door was locked, another indication of an inside job.

It seems pretty conclusive. Joey had been the only physically capable person in a house cut off by a blanket of untrampled snow. But, as you view the evidence, something doesn't seem quite right.

Trial Witnesses & Evidence

This crime can be solved with 1 clue.

Prosecution Witness, Reggie Long

PROSECUTION: How long after the shot did it take you to look out the window to the victim's door?

REGGIE LONG: No time at all. I was right by the window.

PROSECUTION: And after that, how long was the door out of your sight?

REGGIE LONG: Ten seconds maximum. Just long enough to grab my coat and keys and head out the door.

PROSECUTION: And while you were watching, no one left the Goode house?

REGGIE LONG: No one.

PROSECUTION: Now, Mr. Long, about the will. You acted as a witness on the night before the murder.

REGGIE LONG: Correct. Arthur called me up and asked me to come over. It was quite late. He explained that I was witnessing Gus's signature. Gus was in a mean mood, mean but very aware of what he was doing. It just took a minute.

Prosecution Witness, Arthur Ames

ARTHUR AMES: Just like Reggie, I heard the gunshot and the shout. I had an instant feeling it might be Gus. Without thinking, I rushed right out the door, straight into the snow. It wasn't easy going. Some of the drifts were 2 feet high. I got to Gus's door about the same time Reggie came out. I saw absolutely no one but Reggie outside, not until the police showed up a minute or so later.

PROSECUTION: Do you remember seeing any footprints at all, other than your own?

ARTHUR AMES: There were no other prints.

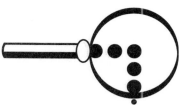

Defense Witness, Investigating Officer

DEFENSE: Did you find any trace of an intruder?

INVESTIGATING OFFICER: We're not sure. You see, in the hall closet we found four coats—three large males and a medium female. Also, three pairs of snow boots, two male and a female, and a pair of rubbers. The rubbers and one of the male coats were wet, as was the floor in front of the closet. We asked Mrs. Goode to identify the coats, and she could not be sure which ones belonged to her husband and nephew. If one of the men owned two coats and a pair of rubbers, then no, there was no intruder. On the other hand, an intruder could have arrived just as it started snowing, hung up his coat, killed Goode, then somehow got away, leaving his coat and rubbers behind. Theoretically.

PROSECUTION CROSS-EXAMINATION: How many keys exist to the front door?

INVESTIGATING OFFICER: Three. Mrs. Goode is positive about that. We've accounted for all three. One was in Joey Goode's pocket, one on the deceased's key chain, and one in Mr. Long's possession, the one used to unlock the door.

PROSECUTION: And was there any way of locking that door without a key?

INVESTIGATING OFFICER: No.

Prosecution Witness, Medical Examiner

MEDICAL EXAMINER: Death was administered by a single shot from an unregistered .38 revolver. The bullet pierced the forehead, passing through both the frontal lobe and postcentral gyrus and lodging in the parietal lobe. I would have to say that death was nearly instantaneous.

Prosecution Exhibit C, Old Will

The Prosecution introduces the contents of Gus Goode's old will. In the absence of any later document, this testament is legally binding. In this will, Gus leaves the bulk of his estate to his wife and nephew, evenly divided between them, with a smaller inheritance going to his lawyer and childhood friend, Arthur Ames. Small bequests are also allocated to other friends and distant relatives.

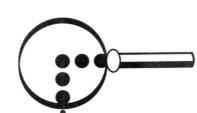

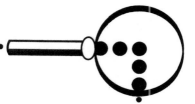

A FAMILY FEUD

Dr. Philip Bromley was overseeing the admission of his patient to Mt. Cedar Hospital. "It's a broken tibia," he told the administrator as he showed her the X rays. "I put Kurt McCoy in an inflatable leg cast. He can't walk on it. He'll need at least a day's rest and observation. To be honest, the fracture was a result of a fight between Mr. McCoy and his cousin. Until things cool down between the McCoys, I just think it better for Kurt to stay here."

Kurt and Emil McCoy had jointly inherited the family garment business, but their relationship soon deteriorated. The latest indecent was a slugfest during which Emil swore that he would kill Kurt and then proceeded to smash his lower left leg with a baseball bat. Kurt needed some place safe to stay while he recovered from the trauma and worked out a lawsuit against his cousin. Hence, Mt. Cedar.

Dr. Bromley wheeled Kurt into his private room and made sure the window was latched. It was 8 P.M. The hospital ordered a security guard to monitor the hall and made a note on Kurt's chart not to disturb him until morning.

At around 2 A.M. a nurse ignored that note and poked her head into room 507. She saw no trace of her patient but did notice an open window. A deflated leg cast on the sill prompted her to peer out the window. Nothing was on the fire escape. But below it, in the deserted alley, lay the body of Kurt McCoy face down on a pile of garbage bags.

The police initially assumed that Kurt had removed his cast and was tying to maneuver his way down the fire escape when he lost his balance. But that was before they saw the bullet hole. A .38 slug had penetrated the victim's chest and proved to be the cause of death.

Emil was interviewed the next day at McCoy Fashion's office and warehouse in an industrial section of town. Emil showed no grief at the news. "Well, at least he won't be suing me." When asked for his whereabouts between 9 P.M. and midnight, Emil had his answer ready. "I was here in the office. We were having trouble with our Hong Kong suppliers. I was calling them or they were calling me all night long. I picked up my car at about 1 A.M. Feel free to check with the phone company

and the garage man."

When the grand jury convenes two weeks later, it's not Emil who stands accused of killing Kurt McCoy. It's the doctor.

PROSECUTION: The Prosecution will point out the discrepancies in Dr. Bromley's story. Kurt McCoy died between 9 and midnight. According to the guard in the hall, Dr. Bromley visited Mr. McCoy at 12:30, at least half an hour after he'd been dead, and made this notation on his chart: "12:30. Resting peacefully." And yet at that time, McCoy was already dead. The doctor has no explanation for this except to say that the coroner must be wrong. *(The district attorney counts off on his fingers.)* The door was guarded, the window locked. The victim feared for his life and trusted only Dr. George Bromley. Only Dr. Bromley had access. And he lied about Mr. McCoy being alive at 12:30.

DEFENSE: The Prosecution has no evidence. My client had no motive. He owns no gun, nor was any gun found among his possessions. The guard, who'd been outside the room all during Dr. Bromley's 12:30 visit, heard no sound. No gunshots, no struggle. Nothing. This grand jury should never have been called.

Your job as a grand jury is not to judge the guilt or innocence of Dr. Bromley but to determine whether or not there is enough evidence to hold him for trial. Despite this simple directive, you cannot help looking at the larger picture. How exactly did Kurt McCoy die and who killed him?

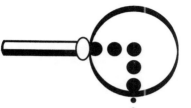

Trial Witnesses & Evidence

This crime can be solved with 2 clues.

Prosecution Witness, Officer on the Scene
PATROLMAN ENGELS: I was the first to arrive in the alley at 2:14 A.M. The body of the victim, Kurt McCoy, was face down on some garbage bags. The body was cool to the touch and totally naked except for a wristband identifying the patient and his room number. An hour or so later, when the coroner allowed the body to be moved, I noticed that there was little blood on the bags, less than I'd imagine given the nature of the wound. We also found no blood in Mr. McCoy's room. Underneath the body were several broken pieces of glass, probably from a drinking glass.

Coroner's Report
The coroner reads from his report and states that the time of death was definitely between 9 P.M. and midnight.

CORONER: Death was caused by a single gunshot wound to the chest, severing the right coronary artery and causing the victim to quickly bleed to death. Other damage to the body included a severely fractured fibula [bone] in the lower left leg. The tibia [bone] was bruised but not broken.

Prosecution Witness, Telephone Technician
In an attempt to eliminate Emil McCoy, the only other principal suspect, the Prosecution calls Bruce Turner, a telephone company technician. Mr. Turner, who reviewed records from the night of the murder, states that Emil McCoy had definitely been speaking on his office instrument.

BRUCE TURNER: No cellular phones had been used to transmit or receive any of the calls. Neither had any special services, such as call-forwarding, been used to mask the destination of an incoming call. The longest time elapsing between calls was approximately 20 minutes.

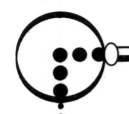

PROSECUTION: And, with no traffic, the McCoy office and warehouse are approximately 15 minutes away from Mt. Cedar Hospital.

Defense Witness, Mrs. Barbara Connor (Room 407)

DEFENSE: Mrs. Connor, you were a patient in the room directly below Mr. McCoy's. Did you see or hear anything the night of the murder that might be of interest to this court?

BARBARA CONNOR: I suppose. You see, I woke up late. It was a warm night and my window was open. Anyway, I reached out for some water on the nightstand. I was kind of groggy, and when I stuck out my hand I brushed my glass of water out the window. That woke me up. I got up and looked out to see if it had hit anybody.

DEFENSE: And what did you see?

BARBARA CONNOR: Well, right below my window was this alley. There were some garbage bags there. My glass landed on top of a bag and had broken into a couple of pieces. There was no body in the alley, just the bags.

DEFENSE: And when did this take place?

BARBARA CONNOR: I checked my clock just before going back to sleep. It was exactly 12:12.

The Prosecution seems eager to cross-examine the witness, but since this is only a grand jury, it does not have the opportunity.

Prosecution Witness, Nurse on Duty

The nurse who entered Kurt McCoy's room testifies that she looked out the window and discovered the body at 2 A.M. She was impressed by the fact that the victim was naked, and this led her to check around. She found Kurt McCoy's hospital clothes neatly piled on a chair. Looking into the closet of his hospital room, she found that Mr. McCoy's street clothes were missing, as were his wallet and keys. His crutches were still propped against the wall where she had last seen them. A police witness confirms later that the victim's street clothing was never found.

PROSECUTION: Did anything unusual happen that evening, before you discovered the body?

NIGHT NURSE: Yes. I was on the second floor at about 1:30, taking a break, when I noticed a man wandering around the halls. He seemed to be checking the room numbers on the doors. Before I could call out to him, he disappeared down a flight of stairs.

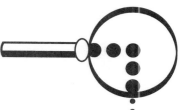

ONE STRIKE, YOU'RE OUT

The Prosecutor was doing her best to make the meek bantamweight look like a monster.

PROSECUTION: Glen Weaver's plan was diabolically simple. For weeks, the neighborhood of Regal Park had been plagued by burglaries. But Glen's wife, Dora, wasn't worried. A first-rate alarm system protected their home. Then, so very conveniently, on the morning of her murder, the alarm broke down. Dora stayed home from work that day waiting for a repairman who never showed up, a repairman that her husband had never called. And with good reason. For if the alarm had been fixed, Glen Weaver would never have been able to bludgeon his wife to death and try to blame it on a nonexistent burglar.

The murder had been discovered by Jimmy and Johnny Hall. At 5:30 P.M., the teenage brothers had just started batting baseballs in the park behind the Weaver home. Jimmy hit a long one and, as bad luck would have it, they heard the shattering of glass. Being honest boys, Jimmy and Johnny began walking toward the row of houses. A man in the house next door had also heard the crash. He came out onto his patio and looked around. "Looks like you boys are going to have to deal with Dora Weaver," he said, pointing to the kitchen door in the Weaver house. There was a hole in the lower left of the door's window. The man joined the boys and was about to knock on the door when he happened to glance through the window. "Good heavens!" Dora Weaver was lying in the middle of the kitchen, her head surrounded by a pool of blood.

Both the neighbor and the boys stared at the body, then glanced up. Glen Weaver was standing in the dining-room doorway, a bloody rolling pin clutched in his hand. He seemed dazed and shocked. On seeing the three faces in the window, Glen dropped the weapon and hurried away. "Where's my ball?" Jimmy asked as he scanned the kitchen floor. His brother told him to shut up.

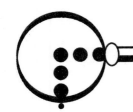

PROSECUTION: The Defense is going to tell you that Glen Weaver had just arrived home from work, that he had just poured himself a scotch in the living room, that he heard the crash of glass and that when he walked into the kitchen, his wife's body was already there. They're going to tell you that a stunned Mr. Weaver picked up the rolling pin, not realizing that it was the murder weapon.

    Well, our response is simple. We will show that the Weaver home had been sealed, every door and window locked from the inside. Even if Mrs. Weaver had admitted her killer, she couldn't very well have bolted the door after he left. Plus, there was no sign of forced entry. A witness, Mrs. Weaver's aunt, was in the house, in her wheelchair by a second-floor window. She will testify that no one even approached the front door until Glen Weaver unlocked it at 5:25 P.M.

    The evidence is simple and straightforward. Had it not been for the baseball, Glen Weaver would have had all the time he needed to wipe his prints off the rolling pin, force a door or window and create the charade of a brutal murder occurring during a robbery attempt. Thank heavens for baseball! It's baseball that will help us convict a cold-blooded killer.

    The Defense waives its opening statement and you feel sorry for little Mr. Weaver. He certainly doesn't look cold-blooded. But if he didn't kill his wife, who did?

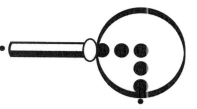

Trial Witnesses & Evidence

This crime can be solved with 2 clues.

Prosecution Witness, Dora's Aunt

PROSECUTION: Ms. Burden, did you see Mr. Weaver come home?

DORA'S AUNT: Yes. I was sitting by my window. Glen came home about 5:25 in the evening.

PROSECUTION: Did you hear any noises from downstairs? The attack on your niece? The sound of breaking glass?

DORA'S AUNT: No. I'd turned my hearing aid off.

PROSECUTION: Was Mr. Weaver aware that you often turned off your hearing aid?

DORA'S AUNT: Yes. He was the one who suggested it. I hate street noise.

PROSECUTION: So, Glen Weaver knew you would not be able to hear when he attacked his wife?

DEFENSE: Objection.

JUDGE: Objection sustained.

DEFENSE CROSS-EXAMINATION: How do you manage to get up and down the stairs?

DORA'S AUNT: The staircase is equipped with an electric riding chair. There's a wheelchair at the bottom that I can lift myself into. It takes effort, but I can manage.

DEFENSE: So, you can move between floors if you really have a need to?

DORA'S AUNT: Yes.

Prosecution Witness, Burglar Alarm Repairman

REPAIRMAN: According to our records, we never received a call from Mr. Weaver about a breakdown. We've been getting a lot of work lately on account of the burglaries in the area.

PROSECUTION: Did you install the Weaver system?

REPAIRMAN: Yeah, about 3 months ago. It was a silent alarm that automatically rang the police. Mrs. Weaver didn't want any obvious signs that the house was protected. We told her the more obvious

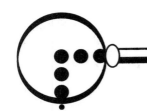

the alarm, the more it would discourage burglars. But she thought alarm strips and wires were ugly.

PROSECUTION: Did you inspect the alarm system after the murder?

REPAIRMAN: Yes. Some wires had jiggled loose in the connection box. A 2-minute repair job.

Prosecution Witness, Robert Jenkins (Neighbor)

The witness describes events leading up to his discovery of the body, including Glen Weaver's appearance and actions when he saw him in the kitchen. On cross-examination, Jenkins admits that Weaver's behavior could also be in keeping with his story that the accused was stunned and picked up the bloody rolling pin by accident.

DEFENSE: Is it true, Mr. Jenkins, that on the evening of the murder you rushed out to a building supply store and insisted that they open up for you so that you could buy a new kitchen door?

ROBERT JENKINS: Yes. I bought a reinforced steel door without a window.

DEFENSE: And why did you do that?

ROBERT JENKINS: My old door was pretty flimsy, and I wanted protection, especially after what happened to Dora.

DEFENSE: So, despite what you saw, you thought Mrs. Weaver had been attacked by a burglar and not by Mr. Weaver. That's what your actions seem to indicate.

ROBERT JENKINS: I guess so.

Defense Witness, Officer on the Scene

OFFICER: Mr. Glen Weaver reported the crime at 5:34 P.M. He said he had just come home. He'd heard glass breaking but could not tell where it came from. He went back into the kitchen and that's when he found his wife. At 5:35 we received a similar call from Mr. Robert Jenkins next door. Me and my partner arrived at 5:40. Jimmy and Johnny Hall were on the front lawn. Mr. Weaver was upstairs with the victim's aunt. He came down to let us in.

The first thing I saw when I entered the kitchen was Dora Weaver lying on her back. There was a bloody concussion on her left temple, indicating she had been attacked from the front. The rolling pin was by the dining-room door. There were signs of a

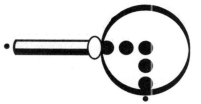

struggle: torn clothing, things knocked off counters. There were also glass fragments on the floor by the back door. Oh, and the baseball, beside the body about a foot away.

DEFENSE: In your opinion, were there any signs of a burglary?

OFFICER: No obvious signs. No.

Prosecution Witness, Dora Weaver's Sister

KAREN LANGFORD: I loved Dora, but she was always a bit of a shrew. Poor henpecked Glen put up with an awful lot. It's no wonder he finally snapped.

DEFENSE CROSS-EXAMINATION: How long were they married?

KAREN LANGFORD: Fifteen years.

DEFENSE: If things were so bad, why didn't they get a divorce?

KAREN LANGFORD: Dora talked about divorce. But Glen always wound up apologizing for things that were Dora's fault, and somehow they stayed together.

DEFENSE: Were there any reasons that he shouldn't have divorced her? Money? Children?

KAREN LANGFORD: No.

DEFENSE: So, maybe the reason they stayed together was because he loved her.

KAREN LANGFORD: Maybe.

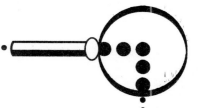

JURY DELIBERATIONS

Stories are arranged alphabetically.

"Death & the Single Girl" Deliberations

The first thing the jury examines is the torn photo. This Christmas photo was obviously taken before Ginger moved to town last April. You and other jury members theorize that it was a picture of Ginger and her *previous* boyfriend and that Ginger herself tore off the half she no longer wanted. This leads to another theory, that it was Ginger's previous boyfriend and not Todd who was scheduled to meet her on the night of the murder.

You shift focus to Paul Gruber and the discrepancies in his story. For instance, Paul initially described Ginger's apartment as "deadly quiet." Yet, as he was leaving, Paul said he could hear running water and used this excuse to turn off the bathroom faucets.

Most jury members have no idea of what part the wet towels played, but the fact that they were found in the garbage with the gloves links them to the murder. Their location, stuck between Paul's floor and Ginger's, further implicates Paul. Or possibly Archie.

Going in Paul's favor is the fact that Ginger told the doorman she was expecting a guest. Since Paul and Archie lived in the building, they would not have to be admitted. And had the doorman really been on duty all evening or not? Another discrepancy.

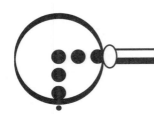

"A Family Feud" Deliberations

The broken glass under the body lends credence to the testimony of the patient in room 407. If there had been a body in the alley at 12:12 A.M., then the glass would have been found on top of it, not underneath. The lack of blood in the room and the minimal amount in the alley supports the same conclusion. Kurt McCoy was killed elsewhere and moved after death.

Since the guard stated emphatically that no one but Dr. Bromley had entered the room, whoever else entered or left the room must have done so through the window, which had been latched from the inside.

Had Kurt really been resting comfortable at 12:30 as Dr. Bromley said? If so, then the coroner was wrong about the time of death. In addition, which leg bone had been broken? The fibula, according to the coroner's report, or the tibia, according to Dr. Bromley's X-ray? Dr. Bromley may not be the killer, but he certainly seems to be hiding something.

Other facts seem equally mysterious. Why was the body naked? Why were the victim's street clothes, wallet, and keys missing? And who was that man wandering around the second floor of the hospital around 1:30 the night of the murder?

"The Haunted House Murder" Deliberations

In the jury room you spend a few hours reviewing physical evidence. The animal blood seems particularly problematic.

Just as confusing is the second knife, which was supposedly carried by the figure Anne saw in the hall. Since this knife was found nearby and had been in contact with the same type of animal blood, this broken weapon appears to be connected to the crime. A fellow juror suggests Lilly had stumbled onto some kind of ritualistic ceremony involving animal sacrifice.

While the crime scene evidence shows that the defendant had been in the room, it does not connect Billy Willis directly to the crime. In fact, the lack of bloody fingerprints on the grisly scene is a point in his favor. The defendant's alibi also seems plausible. If a drunk buys alcohol at 11 P.M., chances are good that he will begin drinking right away. By midnight, Willis could well have been much too drunk to be capable of committing such a strenuous act.

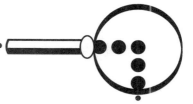

A female juror points out a discrepancy between the way the police described the knife's position and the way the Prosecution described it in her opening statement. You review the transcripts but draw no conclusions about what this means.

"The Hot Designer" Deliberations
The first thing you and fellow jurors focus on is the cause of death. Despite the evidence of the beach umbrella, several jurors doubt that a simple house fire could be intense enough to inflict that kind of damage to the body. Fried nerves? That seems very hot, indeed. And why was there no evidence of smoke inhalation?

A fellow juror points out the absurdity of making a cell-phone call from a house filled with regular phones. But then, fashion people are a little absurd to start with. And the Defense's obsession with the cellular phone mystifies you. Even if the charred telephone belonged to someone else, Ms. Vanushka had still made a call from her own phone to her secretary from 7:53 to 8:05 P.M. This has been documented by the secretary herself. To doubt this is to conclude that the secretary is lying about who called her. Why would she do that?

"The Lady in the Dumbwaiter" Deliberations
The fact that Katrina Burghar mentioned the sound of the fake diamonds being dripped down the chute points to her innocence. But her story about playing with the dumbwaiter just for a lark is highly suspect, given her black silk dress. A much more likely story is that she had an assignation with someone on the second or third floor and saw the dumbwaiter as a way of secretly gaining access.

Other jurors are just as confused as you are by the details. For instance, Lord Dudley saw an intruder in the garden and his bedroom window was open on a chilly night. Yet no trace of an intruder was found. In addition, the upward angle of the two shots would have put Dudley and his killer in very odd positions. The multiple scratches on the drawer, gun handle, and trigger also have to be explained somehow.

But the most confusing aspect of the crime concerns the Asprey Whites. Why had someone constructed paste forgeries and then thrown those forgeries down the chute? And what about the real Asprey Whites? What ever happened to them?

"No Brake for the Wearys" Deliberations

Female jury members agree that the prenuptial agreement was unfair. A young, desirable woman married to an extremely wealthy elderly man deserved more than $200,000 in a divorce settlement.

Male jury members, however, concentrate on the oil change. What about the lack of used oil, oily rags, and oilcans? This seems to incriminate Adam. The fresh oil stain on the floor, however, does seem to support his story.

When discussing cars, a jury member poses an interesting question: How could Adam have known that the Wearys would be using only one car? Since the couple had separate plans for the rest of the day, it seems logical that they would have used both cars.

You and other jury members focus on the condition of Pauline's body. What is the significance of the severe contusion that occurred prior to death, probably suffered on the path from the house to the garage? The state of her dress and the presence of blood on the path also point to this conclusion. Pauline evidently had been injured prior to getting in the car.

The receipt found in the Cadillac seems to give Adam a viable alibi. But if Adam did not tamper with the car, who did?

What really happened on the afternoon of May 15? Is Adam Weary guilty or not? Your jury has been arguing for two days.

"One Strike, You're Out" Deliberations

As you confer, you agree that the most disturbing aspect of this case is the apparent lack of motive. Glen Weaver seemed to have no reason, financial or otherwise, to murder his wife of 15 years. But if Glen didn't kill her, then who did? And why? The only other person in the locked house was Dora's aunt. The aunt could move between floors by herself. But remember, there was a struggle. The aunt would probably not be the winner in any fight with her niece.

One juror nominates the alarm-system repairman. What if he were the neighborhood burglar? He could have let himself into the house, perhaps with the key he had made on his previous visit. Who would make a better burglar than a security specialist? And it would also increase demand for his legitimate business. A nice theory, but there seems little evidence to support it.

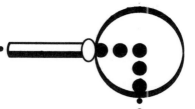

Another juror suspects that Mr. Jenkins knows more than he's telling. Why was he so desperate to replace the back door of his house? Was he afraid of something? Or someone?

You, personally, wonder about the baseball. Why didn't Jimmy Hall see it when he looked around the kitchen floor?

"Our Man in the Field" Deliberations

The Prosecution has established that Okan was the unmasked robber, you and other jury members agree. Okan had been killed by the guard and was being dragged across the field by the accused. The dragging, however, presents problems. You need to consider that the bloody path leads to the center of the field, well beyond the spot where Heath was caught with the body. Also, both the shovel and car were clean of the deceased's blood, clothing fibers, and hair. Heath, you conclude, must have been dragging the body *to* his car, and not from it.

Although the Defense may not realize it, Wally Heath's laundry helps confirm his alibi. The dirty water indicates that Wally Heath started the cycle after 8:55. Most wash cycles are 30 to 40 minutes long. Since the bank alarm went off at 9:08 and the bank was 7 miles from the defendant's house, he could not have both robbed the bank and been at home to put the laundry in the washer.

The only really incriminating piece of evidence, which had shocked Heath's attorney, was the discovery of human blood in the laundry room, in the kitchen, and outside the back door.

"Trial of the Black Widow" Deliberations

You wonder, with other jury members, how you could poison someone at a garden party. Could it have been a random act of buffet terrorism? Or had the poison been intended for someone else? You quickly put these thoughts aside. That's not your job. You're here to evaluate the innocent or guilty of one person, Anabel Lee Ricolah. The only hard evidence in this case is the trace of cyanide found in the plastic storage bag and on the grass.

JUROR: Can we trust Emma Peters as a witness? If we can, then we know that Anabel had contact with at least two storage bags, the one used to hold the drink garnishes and the one found in the electric ice cooler.

SECOND JUROR: That doesn't get us anywhere. Cyanide is a fast poison. There was no garnish in Victor's drink and he had been sipping it for a half-hour.

THIRD JUROR: The poison was in liquid form. It would have been hard to plant on a dry food like a potato chip. Hard but not impossible.

You decide to ask for the videotape from the bailiff and watch it again, hoping it will provide some inspiration. Anabel did buy liquid cyanide, and she certainly has a history of different names and dead husbands. But does that prove she's a killer?

"The Vanishing Verrocchio" Deliberations

When the case came to trial, the statue was still missing. You and a few other jury members feel uneasy about convicting anyone until after the Verrocchio sculpture is recovered. Also, several nagging questions cast doubt on Father Damien's guilt. Why, for instance, would he disguise himself with a hood and wear his own robe? And why would he throw his own robe over the wall rather than simply wearing it back to the manor house? And what about the Chinese pot? Why would Father Damien take a Chinese pot and put it out on the lawn? Why would anybody?

Other nagging questions focus attention on Edgar Chipping, the dead guard. Although he pointed in the defendant's direction, Edgar never directly accused Father Damien. And then there were his last words: "Priest stole. Here. Understand." Was he able to see the face inside the concealing hood? And what did he want them to understand?

"Will-o'-the Wisp" Deliberations

You enter the jury room mulling over mounds of questions and inconsistencies. For starters, who shouted a split second after the murder? Since the victim was killed instantly, it couldn't have been he. The killer perhaps? An eyewitness? It certainly wasn't the deaf-mute defendant, Joey Goode.

Another juror points out a discrepancy between Arthur Ames's testimony and Reggie Long's. You didn't notice the discrepancy until she outlined it. But you still don't understand what it means.

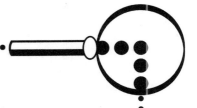

And what about the disappearing wills? No trace of what would have been a multipage document was found anywhere in the snowbound house. Next door, at Arthur Ames's house, the lawyer and police also found nothing.

The final mystery is the lack of footprints in the snow. How would a killer or thief get into the Goode house on a snowy morning?

"A Witless Eyewitness?" Deliberations

You and other jury members combine the forensic evidence with the testimony of the two witnesses in the bar and agree with the Defense. The alley was the scene of the crime, and the time, 5:40 P.M.

Since there is no evidence indicating that Busby and the bartender are in collusion, you also conclude that both are innocent. Nevertheless, Busby's behavior seems noteworthy. He was in an unexpectedly good mood, and despite financial straits he ordered an expensive scotch. Several jurors want to connect this to the defendant's withdrawal of $10,000 from his bank.

The large amount of nitrate on Wade's hand proves that he had fired a weapon, while the trace of nitrate on the deceased's hand and in his pocket indicate that he had handled a fired gun, perhaps carrying it in his pocket. The distance of 8 feet between the gun and the victim goes against the theory of self-defense.

Despite all this, Alice Gabriel's testimony is hard to dismiss. The gunpowder smell mentioned by the police supports her story. She also seems to have no reason to lie. Perhaps she simply misinterpreted what she saw.

VERDICTS

Stories are arranged alphabetically.

"Death & the Single Girl" Verdict

Since there is not enough evidence to convict, you and the jury quickly find Todd Iona *not guilty.*

You, however, have an interesting idea about wet towels and running water and you report it to the district attorney. A week later, the local papers announce the arrest of Archie Gill.

Following your lead, the police discovered that Archie and Ginger had been seriously involved and that Ginger moved to town to get away from him. A few months later Archie followed and, unknown to Ginger, moved in directly below her. One day, he approached her in the park. Ginger was frightened but agreed to a meeting at her place. It was during this confrontation that Archie knifed his ex-sweetheart to death.

Only after Archie went downstairs to clean up did he notice the missing button. And then he recalled Ginger pulling at his shirt. Archie knew he had to return to the scene and account for the incriminating button before the police arrived. Paul had once mentioned having a key to Ginger's apartment. Somehow Archie had to get him to open her door. He didn't call the doorman because he wasn't sure what the building protocol was. He might not have been allowed to accompany the doorman inside.

Archie removed the cheap acoustic tile from the bathroom ceiling of his and Paul's apartment and placed three sopping wet towels on top

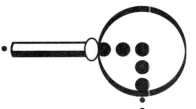

of it. When Paul came home, the towels provided a realistic impression of a bathroom leak from the apartment upstairs.

It didn't matter whether Ginger's sink was overflowing or not. The leak could just as easily have come from another source. But, finding himself alone in the bathroom, Archie turned on the faucets and blocked the overflow drain. By the time Paul and Archie finished inspecting the body and Archie had played his pop-the-button charade, the flood had developed enough to be convincing.

"A Family Feud" Verdict

Even though you don't believe Dr. Philip Bromley is guilty of murder, you do believe he is involved somehow, and that's sufficient reason for you to *remand him to trial.*

When this verdict is announced, Dr. Bromley turns white and volunteers a confession.

DR. PHILIP BROMLEY: I know I could lose my license, even go to jail. Anyway, Kurt McCoy came to me after his fight. He was intending to sue his cousin for assault. When I told him his leg wasn't broken, he asked me if there was any way we could fake a broken leg. He would pay me half of whatever he won. So I dusted off some old X rays and had Kurt admitted. I had no idea he was planning anything more than a little fraud.

That night I happened to be at the hospital seeing another patient. I looked in on Kurt at 12:30 and found his room empty. I didn't know what to do; so, I pretended he was still there. Raising the alarm would have simply drawn attention to the fact that he could walk.

It seemed pretty simple. Kurt was using me. Shortly after I gave the "Do not disturb" order, he must have taken off his cast, climbed out the window, and found a way to get to Emil's office, maybe a cab. He caught Emil there and tried to kill him. Emil must have turned the tables and killed Kurt instead.

Seeing the wristband, Emil deduced that Kurt must have sneaked out. After 1 A.M., when the streets were deserted, Emil drove the corpse back in his own car. By wandering the halls, he figured out where room 507 was and planted the corpse beneath the window. If Kurt had been found wearing street clothes, then

people might conclude he had left the hospital willingly. So, Emil stripped the body, then broke Kurt's leg for real. Funny. Kurt worked so hard to give himself an alibi and all he wound up doing was giving his killer an alibi.

"The Haunted House Murder" Verdict

You find Billy Willis *not guilty.*

Egged on by your verdict, the district attorney kept the case open and eventually amassed enough evidence to prosecute Anne Kincaid. After hours of questioning, the 17-year-old broke down and confessed. For years, Anne had been jealous of her sister. Lilly got everything: praise and attention and, most galling of all, a first-rate education that their parents had saved years for.

It was Lilly who had thought up the prank. They would lure their boyfriends into the old mansion and then scare them with a murder, just as in the movies. Anne instantly saw how this fake murder could be turned into a real one. Lilly and their parents would pay for their favoritism. And Anne would be the one to go to Princeton.

During their exploration, Lilly tiptoed away and set up the grisly scene, smearing herself with chicken blood and sticking the broken-off knife into her blouse. Anne made sure the boys didn't get too close to the "body," at the same time making sure that she got a sufficient amount of blood on herself.

The only thing Anne needed now was a few moments alone with her sister. As soon as she'd tricked the boys into running off, Anne produced a real knife and stabbed Lilly to death. The second scream had also come from Lilly, and this time she wasn't acting. In the 30 seconds it took the boys to run back upstairs, Anne had wiped off the fake knife and thrown it out the window.

The chicken blood helped set the police on the right track. But the clincher was the murder weapon's position. Both Mark and Larry described the handle-grip as facing down. The police photos, however, showed it facing up. Someone had obviously removed the knife and reversed it. Or stuck in a new knife, one with a blade.

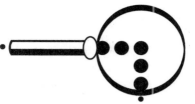

"The Hot Designer" Verdict
You find Harve Grant *not guilty.*

In a note to the district attorney, you encourage his office to check the burned mansion for a large food freezer. The police find just such a freezer. Inside they discover frozen hair strands matching the victim's. An interrogation of Ms. Vanushka's secretary produces a confession.

SECRETARY: All right. Vera died four days before the fire. We were on the beach together, Manny, Vera, and I, when a storm suddenly came up. As we were carrying our things back, a bolt of lightning struck her beach umbrella. Killed instantly. Just a few feet from the house. The servants were all on vacation. No one else had seen it happen, just Manny and me.

We were devastated. Her death had occurred at the worst possible time. VDNY was days away from its public offering. Manny and I both owned stock. If knowledge of Vera's death could only be postponed, we could sell our shares and be rich. So we invented Vera's summer cold and for the next three days fooled everyone into believing she was alive. The freezer kept the body from deteriorating.

It was Manny who engineered the fire. It would thaw her out and disguise the lightning damage. Even the fried beach umbrella would be accepted as a natural result of fire. Manny laid out the body, rigged the toaster oven, then took Vera's cellular phone, leaving his own phone on the scene.

That night Manny called me on Vera's phone. I pretended it was her. His house is in the same cell, and the phone company had no idea exactly where the call originated. He said this would establish that Vera was still alive. It was all meant to look like an accident. We never intended for Harve to get caught in the middle. I'm glad the jury found him not guilty.

"The Lady in the Dumbwaiter" Verdict
You find Katrina Burghar *not guilty.*

There is only one explanation for the paste diamonds hidden in the chute and the absence of real diamonds. The twelve of you agree on the solution but pledge never to reveal it to anyone. It would only

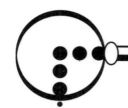

hurt the Dudleys and destroy the upcoming marriage.

Right after the stock-market crash, when Lord Dudley was in desperate need of money, he secretly sold his wife's diamonds and had paste replicas made. Business continued to worsen, however. When his wife discovered their straits, she decided to finally make the sacrifice and sell the Asprey Whites, which she didn't realize he had sold. The only way out for Lord Dudley, it seemed, was suicide. The right kind of suicide would preserve his family's good opinion of him, cancel his debts, and secure a substantial life insurance payoff.

Lord Dudley pretended to see an intruder. Then he disposed of the fakes in the chute and opened his bedroom window, setting the stage for his "murder" and the "burglary." He donned a pair of gloves, took the revolver from his collection, and wedged it into the outer jaw of his bottom desk drawer. Removing the gloves, he then lined up his head with the muzzle and used the poker to press back the trigger. He succeeded on his second attempt. The recoil sent the gun falling down *inside* the open drawer.

Meanwhile, Katrina was hatching her own plot. She was infatuated with her best friend's fiancé and devised the idea of using the dumbwaiter to pull herself up to Captain Batts's room, unseen by family or servants. Your jury is undecided about Batts. Was he a party to her romantic plot, or was she simply planning to surprise him with a knock on the dumbwaiter door? You'll never know.

"No Brake for the Wearys" Verdict
You all agree on reasonable doubt. You find Adam Weary *not guilty*.

A month after the verdict, Adam sells the mansion. The movers discover a diary hidden under Pauline's mattress. In the private journal, the dead woman described her chilling plan to kill her husband and frame her stepson.

As soon as Pauline signed the despised prenuptial agreement, she formed a plot to kill off George and get her hands on all his millions. She planned to invite Adam over and ask him to change the oil, securing his fingerprints on the underchassis of George's Cadillac. Pauline herself would then dispose of the oil-changing equipment and sabotage the brakes, wearing gloves in order to eliminate her prints. After George died in the crash, she would tell the police that she had origi-

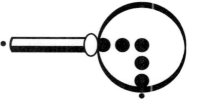

nally planned to ride with him and that Adam had evidently schemed to kill them both.

With this information in hand, the authorities piece together a scenario. Shortly after Adam changed the oil, George took out the car to buy milk and cigarettes. An hour later, Pauline sabotaged the brakes. Then, at about 1:25 P.M., the couple left the house, walking to the garage and their separate cars. But on the path, Pauline accidentally slipped on the wet gravel and fell, knocking herself unconscious.

George was frantic with worry and managed, despite his age, to lift his wife into the Cadillac, intending to drive her to the nearest emergency room. The end result, of course, was that Pauline not only succeeded in killing her husband and framing her stepson, but she also managed to accidentally kill herself.

"One Strike, You're Out" Verdict
You find Glen Weaver *not guilty.*

Your curiosity about Jimmy Hall's baseball leads to an interesting theory. All twelve of you have a private conference with the district attorney. A search warrant produces a horde of stolen goods and a confession from Robert Jenkins, the neighbor.

ROBERT JENKINS: I'm the guy who's been robbing houses. As for the Weavers, I didn't mean to kill nobody. I figured Dora and Glen were still at work. The old lady would be upstairs with her hearing aid off and I'd have the downstairs to myself. I had no idea about the alarm. I'm glad it was off.

So I break in around 5o'clock, smashing the glass in the door so I can reach in for the knob. I barely get inside when Dora barges in. Crazy woman. She sees the broken glass and my gloves and she attacks. I grab the rolling pin to defend myself and... Well, you know.

I don't take anything, I'm too scared. I walk out, then reach in through the hole and bolt the door. I go home to my own kitchen. And then a little while later this baseball comes flying through the glass in my door. I go outside and I see these boys coming with their bats. They're looking around for their ball. I leave my kitchen door open so they can't see the broken window, then point to the

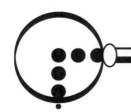

hole in the Weaver window. The rest is all luck, Glen being there just at the right time.

I send the boys out front to wait for the cops, then slip the baseball in beside Dora. The only problem left is *my* broken glass. In the dark you could barely see, but I had to replace it right away. You know how hard it is finding a building supply store open at that hour?

"Our Man in the Field" Verdict

The Prosecution has not proven its case. You find Wallace Heath *not guilty.*

Minutes after the jury foreman reads the verdict, a rookie patrolman, exploring the field behind Wally Heath's house, discovers a body in the abandoned well. It is found to be the remains of Amanda Heath, Wally's missing wife, who had been stabbed to death with a kitchen knife.

Faced with this discovery, Wally breaks down. Two weeks before he had been arrested dragging Okan's body, Wally had yet another explosive domestic quarrel, lost his temper, and killed his wife. He dumped the body into the well and invented the story about Amanda running off with a salesman. Since Amanda had no family and few friends nearby, everyone readily believed Wally's tale.

On the night of the robbery, Wally was in the laundry room when he happened to look out his window. By the light of the full moon, he could see a man drag a body into the field, dumping it only a few dozen yards from the well.

Wally went crazy with worry. The man's body was bound to be discovered. And when it was, the police would make a thorough search, finding Amanda in the process. Wally had no choice. He had to move the new body. If it were found anywhere else, the police would have no reason to scour this little field, and Amanda could rest in peace.

Unfortunately, the county workers saw him in the moonlight just as he began to drag the burglar's body to his car. It was, of course, preferable to be convicted of bank robbery than of murder. So, Wally said nothing to incriminate himself.

In his confession, Wally describes the bank robber's getaway car and the man he saw depositing the body in the field. Judd Okan's cousin is soon arrested on bank-robbery charges.

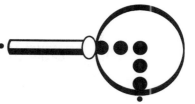

"Trial of the Black Widow" Verdict

You have no choice but to find Anabel Lee Long Lyons Leon Ricolah *not guilty.*

But during your two days of deliberation, you did manage to figure out how she *could* have arranged her husband's poisoning. A day before the party, Anabel could have worked up a special batch of ice cubes.

RECIPE: Fill ice tray one-third-full of water. While it freezes, boil a pan of marbles or some other small objects. Remove ice tray from freezer and place a hot marble in the center of each cube, just long enough to create a depression in the cube. Drain off melted water, then quickly fill the depression with liquid cyanide. Freeze the mixture, then fill the rest of ice tray with water and return to freezer. Keep in a cold, safe place until ready to use.

On the day of the party, Anabel could have filled a plastic bag with her poisoned cubes and stored it in the bottom of the electric cooler, beneath a hundred pounds of real ice. Having herself arranged the paltry supply of limes, she could have conveniently sent the bartender off for more, then mixed Victor's drink, adding her own special ice cubes. She would make sure to taste the drink in front of witnesses, then stay far away from Victor until the ice cubes melted and the cyanide was released. The dead grass could have been caused by Victor spilling the last of his poisoned drink.

Since Anabel wouldn't have had the chance to clean up after herself, she would have had to trust to fate. Remember, this was before anyone suspected murder. A person cleaning out the cooler would have simply tossed out the remaining ice and disposed of the bag.

"The Vanishing Verrocchio" Verdict

You find Father Damien *not guilty.*

As the bailiff read back Edgar's last words, a juror slightly hard-of-hearing heard something a little different. "Priest's hole. Maybe he said 'priest's *hole,*' not 'priest stole.'"

Yes, of course. Another jury member recalls that priests' holes are hiding places found in many old English houses, concealed spaces where

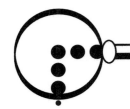

priests once hid from the authorities. Suddenly the case makes sense. The guilty party must be Lord George, the only member of the foursome who would know where a priest's hole could be found in Brighton Manor. You reconstruct the crime.

The earl of Brighton desperately wanted the bust but did not have the available cash. Rather than see it disappear into someone else's collection, he decided to steal it. Disguising himself with a hood and robe, Lord George entered the library, knocking out the guard. He then took the statue from its wooden stand and placed it in the priest's hole, directly under the parquet floor. That's what Edgar had met by "Understand": The priest's hole was *under*neath the *stand*.

The only problem remaining would have been to make it appear as if the statue had been removed from the estate. Lord George obviously knew about the videocamera and made sure that it recorded the image of a priest carrying out a weighted sack. The contents of the sack? The Chinese pot.

Once out on the grounds, Lord George removed the pot, and threw the sack, hood, and robe over the wall, hoping to implicate Father Damien. The guard's dying words made his effort nearly perfect.

The jury sends a note out to the judge and you receive confirmation within the hour. The St. Augustine bust was right where you said it would be, and that's all the proof you needed to find Damien not guilty.

"Will-o'-the-Wisp" Verdict

You find Joey Goode *not guilty*.

A glaring inconsistency guides you along the right path. It is illegal to witness a will in which you inherit. The fact that Arthur Ames signed the new will as a witness meant that *he* had been cut out, not Joey Goode. Suddenly, Arthur has a motive for killing Gus and destroying the new will. With this in mind, you construct the scenario.

On the night before the murder, Gus Goode wrote a new will, disinheriting his old friend and lawyer. The reason? You don't know.

Arthur was angered by Gus's behavior and visited his neighbor the next morning, just as it stopped snowing. Perhaps Arthur intended the meeting to be peaceful, although the unregistered gun in his pocket would indicate otherwise.

Gus and Arthur argued. Arthur brandished the weapon and it went

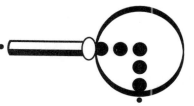

off. The shout was Arthur's, delivered in shocked surprise at his own lethal action. After a minute of indecision, Arthur stuffed the will into his pocket and left, forgetting his overcoat and rubbers in the hall closet. Just as Arthur closed the door, Reggie Long popped out of his front door and naturally assumed Arthur had just arrived. The discrepancy between Reggie and Arthur's testimonies? Reggie said he turned away from his view of the house for only 10 seconds, hardly enough time for Arthur to leave his own house and trudge through the snow to his neighbor's.

Gus's front door was still unlocked. But when Reggie ran up and offered his key, Arthur was quick to take advantage, pretending to unlock an already unlocked door.

The only remaining problem was to make his own copy of the will disappear. Since Arthur was not a suspect, it was relatively easy for him to search through the wrong files and to dispose of the telltale document while the police looked elsewhere.

You aren't surprised when, a week later, Arthur Ames is arrested. After all, the police aren't stupid. They're just a little slower than you.

"A Witless Eyewitness?" Verdict

You and fellow jurors argue endlessly, trying to reconcile Alice Gabriel's story with the rest of the evidence. After three days of deliberation, you finally deliver your verdict, finding Wade Poe *guilty of first-degree murder.*

The key to the case was a passing comment by Wade's wife, stating that he had been doing research on low-lifes and con artists. The mystery, you discover, hinges on an old con game played by Sonny and Busby on the naïve defendant.

The fight and "murder" that Alice witnessed from her window had actually been staged for Wade's benefit. Sonny loaded the silver .22 with blanks, then forced Wade to "kill" him in self-defense. When Busby walked into the apartment a few seconds later, Wade was desperate, prepared to do anything to avoid a murder charge. Busby said he would keep his mouth shut and dispose of Sonny's body for a payment of $10,000. Wade had no choice but to agree.

Wade rushed to his bank and quickly delivered the money to Busby. While Busby was celebrating with a drink at McGregor's, his partner

Sonny was busy disposing of the evidence. But the two con artists had seriously underestimated their pigeon.

After paying off Busby, the writer began to have second thoughts. Had he been the victim of a con, like the cons Sonny and Busby always bragged about? Enraged by the thought, Wade retrieved his gun from his glove compartment and hid himself outside the house. When Sonny emerged, still very much alive, Wade followed him to McGregor's bar. There, in the alley, he confronted his tormentor and shot him to death, this time for real.

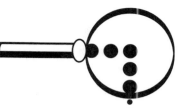

INDEX

Answer pages are in italics.

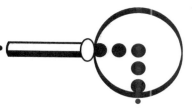